ADAPTATIONS OF
MUSCULAR ACTIVITY

ADAPTATIONS

OF

MUSCULAR ACTIVITY

A Textbook for Adapted Physical Education

by

GENE A. LOGAN

Professor, Southwest Missouri State College

Contributing Author:
JAMES G. DUNKELBERG

Professor, Los Angeles State College

Illustrated by Gene A. Logan

WADSWORTH PUBLISHING COMPANY, INC.

Belmont, California

L.C. Cat. Card No.: 64–18140
Printed in the United States of America

Second printing: August 1965

FOREWORD

Whenever I have the privilege of introducing Gene A. Logan to an audience, I find myself in a multi-dimensional quandary. *Which Gene Logan shall I present?* The scientist? The teacher of adapted physical education? The physical therapist? Or the artist? But in *Adaptations of Muscular Activity* this quandary is at least partly resolved by the fact that the scientist, teacher, therapist, and artist all collaborated in the preparation of Dr. Logan's most recent book.

The scientist chose to treat neuromuscular structure and function from a biophysiological point of view. The teacher and the therapist analyzed the functional relationships between structure and movement, and described the specific exercises that might be used to ameliorate each handicapping condition. The artist delineated the structure-movement relationships in a unique set of anatomical plates and illustrated the exercises with line drawings that display both the scientist's and the artist's understanding of human anatomy and movement. (And it must be noted that these drawings are but a poor shadow of the major work of the artist as a sculptor—but, alas, carved wood and welded metal cannot be fitted between the covers of a book.)

Dr. Logan has been most ably assisted by the contributing authorship of Dr. James G. Dunkelberg. Working together, they have produced a multi-dimensional book that makes a significant contribution to the literature of human movement by providing new insights into the relationships between the structure and the function of the human body.

Eleanor Metheny
University of Southern California

ACKNOWLEDGMENTS

Grateful acknowledgment is made to Dr. James G. Dunkelberg for his contribution of ideas and specific chapters to this book. He was largely responsible for the writing of the following chapters: 3—Adapted Physical Education, 4—Growth and Development of Man, 8—Gravity and Postural Adaptations, 9—Congenital and Pathological Conditions, 13—Selection and Programming of Sports, 14—Organization of the Adapted Program, and 15—Administration of the Adapted Program.

I wish to express my appreciation for detailed criticism of the manuscript and for many valuable suggestions to Dr. Celeste Ulrich, Woman's College, University of North Carolina; Dr. Roger K. Burke, Occidental College; and William M. Fowler, Jr., M.D., Department of Physical Medicine and Rehabilitation, School of Medicine, University of California, Los Angeles. I am indebted to Dr. Wayne C. McKinney, Chico State College, for his generous contribution to the preparation of the manuscript. Appreciation is also expressed to Drs. Eleanor Walsh, San Fernando Valley State College, and Theus Lee Doolittle, Los Angeles State College, for their valuable assistance with the manuscript.

Gratitude is expressed to John T. Starr, University of Wyoming, who prepared the list of books and periodicals. Thanks are offered to Renee Nathanson and Thomas Lile, who served as models for many of the illustrations in the text. To Mrs. Helen Graves, thanks are given for assisting with the typing.

Gene A. Logan

CONTENTS

CONTENTS

1

A POINT OF VIEW

Adaptations of Muscular Activity is concerned with *dynamic man*. It deals with (a) his body structure, functions, and movements; (b) selected factors or forces which affect him and his motor activity; (c) his attempts to adjust to the specific demands of those factors; and (d) how—through the utilization of selected physical activities— he may limit the degree and severity of his adaptation to the demands imposed by gravity, trauma, injury, congenital defect, illness, or disease. Therefore, in order to be of most value, this book must clearly identify the authors' point of view concerning physical education, and the implications of that viewpoint for the professional preparation of teachers of adapted physical education.

Physical education is and should continue to be a scientifically planned and directed program of selected physical activities. Its contributions are unique in the education of the child in terms of the benefits which the individual derives from physical activity, such benefits as strength, endurance, flexibility, relaxation, and skill. The authors' orientation to physical education lies in the biological and physiological factors of physical activity. However, other benefits, such as psychological, sociological, and emotional, that are outcomes of one's biophysiological activity are not ignored. Rather, primary emphasis is placed upon those outcomes that are directly attributed to or are consequences of the individual's physical activity. For it is through one's physical activity that these other values or benefits are derived.

What are the implications of this biophysiological orientation? It implies that the knowledge of anatomy, physiology, kinesiology, and the laws of physical growth and development is utilized as the primary basis for the justification and planning of physical education programs. In addition, the professional preparation of teachers of adapted physical education will be affected insofar as this orientation constitutes an approach not presently emphasized in the literature of this field.

The biophysiological approach has for its primary emphasis the concept of *average* dynamic man. This means that at all times the student must refer to his basic knowledge of the biophysiological structure and functions of man. The student must know the biological, physiological, and kinesiological effects of physical activity of various kinds, duration, and intensity. Frequently, this basic information is provided through specific prerequisite courses in anatomy, physiology, kinesiology, and physiology of exercise.

The student must also have or acquire an understanding and appreciation of those forces that affect man, and of the resulting deviations from the norm. A few examples are (1) the effect of gravity on the lumbar curve, (2) trauma resulting from participation in athletics, (3) congenital defects, and (4) illness and disease such as asthma or cardiovascular deviations. The effects of these forces and their resulting deviations bring about adaptations of muscular activity and should therefore be the basic concern of the teachers of adapted physical education.

In the application of the biophysiological approach, the teacher's function is to utilize his knowledge of average man, the effects of those forces that affect average man, and the demands of various motor activities. Through the application of commonly known principles of exercise, the teacher should be able to select those physical activities that are directed toward the amelioration of the individual's biophysiological adaptations. The forces of gravity, injury, and disease may cause the individual to adapt his movement patterns. The adapted physical education teacher should, therefore, attempt to select physical activities which would aid in the elimination or reversal of those adaptations that are undesirable. It must be remembered that the nature of certain physical limitations necessitates specific adaptations which are essential and should be encouraged.

2

PHYSICAL EDUCATION OF MAN

Physical education provides the opportunity for the development and maintenance of physical fitness. It offers an opportunity for facilitating the normal growth of the child, and it helps to develop, and to prevent the reversal of, such biophysiological factors of performance as strength, endurance, flexibility, relaxation, and skill.

Physical activity in the form of exercise, sports, games, and rhythms provides a setting whereby recreational activities may be learned and enjoyed. Therefore, schools must provide the opportunity for students to experience the satisfactions derived from participation in physical activity. Some of the satisfactions people seek through participation in physical activities are the joy of creation, fellowship, a sense of achievement, emotional experiences, the enjoyment of beauty, and relaxation. The school must be more than a place for the student to participate in a variety of physical activities; it should also offer experiences and activities to form a basis for the development of an interest that will result in the utilization of neuromuscular activity as a leisure-time or avocational pursuit.

Recreation possesses certain characteristics which distinguish it from the other types of activities usually offered in an educational program. Recreation relies upon intrinsic motivation: the person engages in the activity because he desires or chooses to do so without any external compulsion of any type. Another essential characteristic is the immediate and direct satisfaction that the individual experiences as a result of his participation. Recreation can be any form of leisure-time experience or activity through which the individual receives enjoyment or satisfaction. Physical education *activities* are the vehicles through which voluntary activity of a recreational nature can be provided.

Most educators agree that physical education is indispensable in meeting the growth and development needs of the child. The school must assume the responsibility for providing the student with the opportunities, experiences, and physical activities that will contribute toward a more complete education. These physical activities must play an integral part in the over-all educational process of the child.

Physically handicapped children are often deprived of the opportunity to explore safely the real world, their own emotions, and the ideas that come by and through play. Unfortunately, normal play behavior is often limited for the disabled. Ironically, such children have an even greater need for physical activity than do "average" children. The opportunity for medically supervised play must be given to the physically handicapped child in order to help him develop desirable character traits.

Although the emphasis is usually placed upon the physical aspect of the handicapping condition, educators should not lose sight of the emotional involvements that often accompany physical disabilities. The major problems of the handicapped are not only physical, they are social and psychological as well. In a sense, there is no special psychology of the handicapped individual as opposed to the individual without serious physical impairment. But any physical defect, major or minor, can present problems to the individual, in addition to the problems common to all. The degree to which the individual becomes emotionally involved as a result of his handicapping condition is directly related to his personal reaction and the reaction of others with whom he associates.

Adapted physical education is physical education for those individuals with physical limitations. The selection of activities and the implementation of these activities in the program must be based upon sound principles. These principles must utilize the developmental characteristics, readiness, physical status, requirements, and interests of the student, and a thorough knowledge of the activities in order to achieve the objectives of the program. Through adapted physical education, the individual may find ways to make certain social adjustments with his peers, as he is usually homogeneously grouped with other handicapped individuals. Although the emphasis is upon dealing with the physical disability, the adapted physical education class should also serve the handicapped through ancillary means such as socialization and group interaction.

3

ADAPTED PHYSICAL EDUCATION

It is the right of all children in a democratic society to have the opportunity for the fullest development of their abilities through education. This right permits no exceptions. It must embrace all who can profit from instruction. Therefore, the schools have the responsibility of providing the opportunity for the fullest possible development of those aptitudes with which each child is endowed. Those skills, knowledges, attitudes, and habits that are essential to successful living should be developed because each child is entitled to an education that will help him live a full, rich, and useful life. This development is of basic importance to the child and to the community in which he lives.

School administrators are faced with the problem of designing, developing, and administering educational programs to give all children an equal opportunity for education. Educational programs must provide for every child regardless of the nature of his limitations, needs, and capacities, which may be physical, mental, or emotional. Therefore, in addition to the regular educational program designed for average or normal children, the schools must provide specialized programs for those students who are unable to receive maximum benefits from the regular education program.

SPECIAL PHYSICAL EDUCATION

Between 5 and 10 per cent of school-age children need special educational services. Approximately 3 per cent of the children will require such extensive adaptations of their educational programs that they will be enrolled in special schools.

The physically handicapping conditions that most frequently prohibit a student's participation in the regular physical education program may be classified as (1) visual handicaps, (2) auditory handicaps, (3) orthopedic handicaps, (4) cardiovascular conditions, (5) poor body mechanics, and (6) other traumatic, pathological, and congenital conditions.

Because of the nature of these handicapping conditions, it is possible to make some generalizations about the needs of the students who will require special physical education. These students fall into one or more of the following groups: (1) those seeking to adapt themselves to a permanent condition, (2) those desiring to rehabilitate a physical disability, (3) those requiring limited physical activity, and (4) those recommended for a developmental program.[1]

Definition of Adapted Physical Education

The special physical education classes that are provided for those students who are unable to participate in the regular program have a variety of names. Some of the more common are Corrective Physical Education, Remedial Gymnastics, Remedial Physical Education, Exercise Therapy, Corrective Therapy, Developmental Physical Education, Individual Physical Education, and Adapted Physical Education. In 1947, the Committee on Adapted Physical Education of the American Association for Health, Physical Education and Recreation conducted a survey to determine the most acceptable term for the identification of these special classes. Authoritative opinion indicated that the term "Adapted Physical Education" was the most acceptable and that it best described the

---

[1] Gene A. Logan et al., *Student Handbook for Adapted Physical Education* (Dubuque, Iowa: Wm. C. Brown Co., 1960), p. 1.

nature of these classes. The Committee defined Adapted Physical Education as

a diversified program of developmental activities, games, sports, and rhythms, suited to the interests, capacities and limitations of students with disabilities who may not safely or successfully engage in unrestricted participation in the general physical education program.[2]

If one were to read this definition and stop after the word "students," he would have a good descriptive or functional definition of general physical education. It is only when one includes the idea that the students have disabilities that he becomes aware of the specialized nature of these classes.

Objectives of Adapted Physical Education

Acceptance of the concept that adapted physical education is physical education for those individuals who are unable to participate in the general program makes it possible to state a general objective that is applicable to all students: "To provide opportunities for all students to acquire the maximum physiological, psychological and sociological development of which they are capable, through participation in properly selected and controlled physical activities."[3]

Since those students who are assigned to adapted physical education classes have physical conditions which may be thought of as either temporarily or permanently limiting their physical activity, specific objectives for these students should be developed. The following objectives may serve as "guidelines" for determining the nature and scope of adapted physical education:

1. To protect each student's condition from further aggravation by arranging a program of activities within his limitations.
2. To assist the student in understanding and accepting his own limitation.

[2] "Guiding Principles for Adapted Physical Education," *Journal of the American Association for Health, Physical Education and Recreation,* XXXIII, No. 4 (April 1952), 15.
[3] Logan et al., *Student Handbook,* p. 1.

3. To correct or alleviate the student's remediable weaknesses or malalignments.

4. To develop the best possible organic vigor or condition in view of the individual's limitations.

5. To develop skill and knowledge of recreational sports and games suitable or adaptable to the individual's limitations.

6. To develop the student's knowledge and appreciation of good body mechanics and efficiency.

7. To help students make satisfactory social and emotional adjustments to problems imposed by their disabilities.

8. To help students gain security through improved function and increased ability to meet the physical demands of daily living.[4]

Bases for Adapted Physical Education

Textbooks of program planning and curriculum development for physical education indicate that there are two major factors which influence the nature of the regular program. These are (1) the needs and interests of the students, and (2) the philosophy of the school or of the physical education department. Furthermore, the student should have a physical examination beforehand, at which time he should be medically approved for unrestricted participation in the regular program. This program should include participation in a wide variety of team sports, individual and dual team sports, games, rhythmic activities, aquatics, resistive exercises, and calisthenics that are appropriate for students at various developmental levels.

Those students who may not safely or successfully participate in the general program are assigned to the adapted program. The one factor that should have the most influence on the nature of this program and which is the actual basis for the program is *the medical diagnosis and recommendation of the physician.* Adapted physical education programming must be based upon thorough knowledge of the medical status of the student, his individual needs and interests, and the philosophy of the school and department.

The bases for both the general physical education program and the adapted physical education program are very similar. The

---

[4] Logan et al., *Student Handbook,* p. 2.

major difference is the emphasis placed upon the various factors of philosophy, needs, interests, and the physical examination. This relationship is illustrated in Figure 3.1. The broken lines indicate the emphasis on individualization of regular physical education that becomes adapted physical education. Where the regular physical education program is based primarily upon the group char-

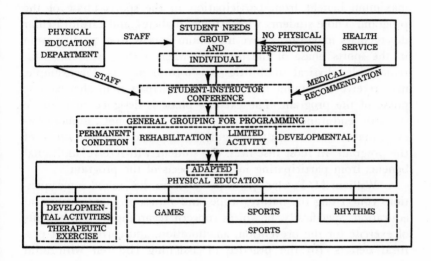

Figure 3.1

acteristics and needs of the students, the adapted physical education program is primarily concerned with the individual needs of the students. In relation to the activities to be utilized in the adapted program, the activities of the regular physical education program are grouped into two major areas, (1) therapeutic exercise and (2) sports.

IMPLICATIONS FOR PROGRAMMING

Students who are assigned to the adapted program fall into one or more of the four general groups previously mentioned. In terms of these groups, certain implications for adapted physical education programming become evident. If the needs of each of these groups are to be met, it is imperative that provision be made to include an exercise phase as well as a sports phase within the adapted physical education program. The sports phase includes games, rhythms, and aquatics. Those students who have a permanent disability, such as cerebral palsy or congenital amputations, or who are severely handicapped visually or aurally may receive maximum benefit from participation in the sports phase of the program. Those students with asthma, diabetes, and cardiovascular divergencies may also receive maximum benefit from participation in the sports phase of the program, whereas those students with remediable physical disabilities or postural defects, for example, may receive maximum benefit from participation in the exercise phase of the program. The exercise phase is designed to improve strength, endurance, and flexibility. One should not assume, however, that a student must be rigidly assigned to only one phase of the program. In most instances, the student will receive additional benefits from participating in both aspects of the program.

William M. Fowler, Jr., a pediatrician, has raised some questions concerning the nature, scope, and values of adapted physical education. Specifically, he voices concern regarding (a) the benefits of exercise for the prevention, amelioration, and correction of postural defects, (b) the practice of assigning children with mild divergencies to the program, and (c) the promises and claims made to the student regarding the correction of his condition. He reminds the reader that if amelioration or correction is possible through prescribed exercises, the program must be initiated early. In addition, he stresses the importance of providing students who have postural defects the opportunity to participate in activities within the regular physical education program.[5]

The programming of students in adapted physical education must be based on the medical recommendations of the physician and on sound principles which are applicable to each child. Some of these principles are that children need activity, recognition, status, self-direction, self-expression, group acceptance, and new and interesting experiences. The major problem is the adaptation of

---

[5] "Functional Postural Deviations in Children and the Relationship of Posture to Physical Health" (unpublished paper, University of California, Los Angeles), pp. 4, 12.

normal activities to meet the specific needs of the individual student. This involves the study and the thoughtful combining of the individual's interests, aptitudes, abilities, previous experiences, and physical limitations to satisfy his particular needs.

The primary purpose of the adapted physical education program is to help prepare the handicapped student to live a full, rich, and satisfying life in a society of nonhandicapped individuals. Therefore, the student should learn those games and sports which are enjoyed by his nonhandicapped peers. The selection of activities for the adapted program should include primarily those games and sports that do not require extensive adaptations of either the rules or the nature of the activity.

The student should be encouraged to return to the regular physical education program whenever his condition permits. The student may be reassigned to a particular phase or activity of the regular program; but it is imperative that the instructor of the class or activity be well informed regarding the nature and extent of the student's condition. The instructor must be cognizant of the limitations of the student within any given physical activity. Those students who are assigned to the adapted program for the rehabilitation of joint injuries are frequently able to be reassigned to the regular physical education program without restrictions.

The role of the adapted physical education instructor is to assist the students to achieve maximum benefit from the therapeutic or sports phases of the program. He not only should encourage but should facilitate the student's return to the regular program whenever possible. Those students whose conditions prohibit reassignment to the regular program he should help to develop interests and skills in recreational activities in which they may participate safely and successfully with their nonhandicapped peers.

Selected References

Clarke, H. Harrison, and David H. Clarke, *Developmental and Adapted Physical Education*. Englewood Cliffs, N.J.: Prentice-Hall, Inc., 1963.

Daniels, Arthur S., *Adapted Physical Education*. New York: Harper & Row, Publishers, 1954.

Dunkelberg, James G., and Gene A. Logan, "New Directions in the Professional Preparation of Teachers of Adapted Physical Education." Paper presented to the Joint Meeting of the Professional Preparation and Adapted Physical Education Sections, Southwest District Convention, American Association for Health, Physical Education and Recreation, Albuquerque, New Mexico, 1961.

Fait, Hollis F., *Adapted Physical Education*. Philadelphia: W. B. Saunders Co., 1960.

Howland, Ivalclare Sprow, *Adapted Physical Education in Schools*. Dubuque, Iowa: Wm. C. Brown Co.. 1959.

Logan, Gene A., et al., *Student Handbook for Adapted Physical Education*. Dubuque, Iowa: Wm. C. Brown Co., 1960.

Mathews, Donald K., Robert Kruse, and Virginia Shaw, *The Science of Physical Education for Handicapped Children*. New York: Harper & Row, Publishers, 1962.

4

GROWTH AND
DEVELOPMENT OF MAN

It is imperative that those who are responsible for guiding the physical education of children have a thorough background of knowledge about the normal physical growth and development of children, since the physical educator plays such a major role in the guidance of that growth and development. Through his knowledge of the principles and laws of these physical processes he selects those activities that are appropriate for children of various ages or developmental levels. The reader who is interested in further study of this area than can be presented here should refer to the books in the fields of child psychology and child growth and development listed in the Appendix.

The term *development* indicates the process through which the child achieves maturity. This process is influenced by or dependent upon the factors of maturation and learning. *Maturation* indicates the appearance or unfolding of innate hereditary traits. The emergence of a trait through maturation is characterized by its involuntary appearance, whereas the evolution of a change in the behavior of the individual as the result of volition is due to the process of learning.

Maturation, however, is an important factor in determining the ability to learn. It provides the raw material for learning and it influences the pattern and sequence of learning. Learning must wait on maturation. An individual cannot learn new skills until he has achieved the necessary physical and mental development; it is these factors that provide the foundation for learning.

CHARACTERISTICS OF PHYSICAL DEVELOPMENT

The developmental process that takes the individual through infancy, childhood, and adolescence to physical maturity is a complex process that is guided and controlled by definite natural laws. The appearance of specific characteristics at specific age levels has led to the following statement of principles concerning human development. These guiding principles are a consensus of those presented in the literature.

Changes Are Quantitative and Qualitative in Nature. Development involves changes in size, proportion, function, and structure. Specifically, *growth* is used to indicate those changes which involve an increase in size or proportion, whereas development, one aspect of the growth process, refers to changes in function or structure.

Development Follows a Pattern That Is Orderly, Continuous, and Predictable. Each step or phase is the outcome of the preceding phase, and each phase is prerequisite for the next. Development continues from the time of conception to the time of maturity. The pace is slow and regular—though, of course, not always the same for everyone. But the general pattern is not altered by the speed of development: all children pass through the same phases or steps at approximately the same time. Since the pattern is so fixed in its sequence, and appears so consistently in the majority of children, it is possible to establish certain standards of expectation for the various age levels. This consistency has led to the establishment of height-weight tables, tests of mental and of social age, and similar measurement tools and standards. Nonetheless, though age-correlated developmental levels are useful for developing norms, they should be applied to individuals only with the greatest caution and professional judgment.

Development Occurs at Different Rates for Different Parts of the Body. Not all parts of the body develop at the same rate, but each proceeds at its own rate and reaches maturity at a different time. For example, the brain attains maximum physical size at approximately six to eight years of age. The hands and feet reach their adult size early in adolescence. This may account in part for the apparent awkwardness and clumsiness of adolescent children. Skeletal growth and ossification continue into the early twenties.

Development Proceeds from General to Specific Responses. In learning a new motor skill, the individual first attempts general or total-body responses that are not required for the performance of the skill. Such irrelevant or even detrimental movements may include exaggerated action of the body, head, or limbs. Through practice, the individual learns to decrease or eliminate the generality and to increase the specificity of responses. The elimination of unwanted movement is possibly the predominant factor in the acquisition of correct skill movement.

Rate of Development Is Influenced by Individual Differences. All children normally pass through each major stage of development, though they do not do so necessarily at the same age. Each child grows at his own rate. Individual differences in over-all growth rate generally remain constant. The accelerated (or the retarded) developer at an early age is likely to be an accelerated (or retarded) developer at a late age also. Significant factors in a child's experience (amount and kind of instruction, opportunity, practice, motivation, and interests) as well as certain environmental factors (improper diet, lack of exercise, injury, or disease) could greatly accelerate or retard his performance capabilities or his motor development. The resultant positive or negative modifications in the developmental timetable are much more significant than the innate influences. Development, however, must wait for prerequisite maturation to occur. A child who is retarded in his performance according to developmental norm tables could make unusual progress. If, for example, retardation is the result of poor environmental influences, the removal or reversal of such influences in order to capitalize completely upon the degree of maturation that is already present could significantly change the rate of development. But early losses in maturation and development can never be entirely "caught up."

CHARACTERISTICS OF SKELETAL GROWTH

Any discussion of the characteristics of skeletal growth must include *Wolff's law* and the *carpal index*. The first accounts for the skeletal development of the bones of the body. Wolff's law states: "Every change in the form and function of a bone, or of their function alone, is followed by certain definite changes in their internal architecture, and equally definite secondary alteration in their external conformation, in accordance with mathematical laws." Wolff's statement has been attacked continuously since its proposal, especially with regard to its phrase, "in accordance with mathematical laws." Steindler, in attempting to acknowledge the effect of stress or pressure upon bony development, has modified Wolff's statement to indicate that the external shape and the internal structure of bone is changed according to the stress involved.[1] In relation to the effect of pressure on bone growth, Mainland concluded from a review of research that constant pressure, even though slight in magnitude, usually causes atrophy. But that intermittent pressure, even though great, seems to result in bone growth. Thus, the small constant gravitational torques resulting from postural deviations may be debilitating to the bone, although the tremendous stresses of sports participation, if less than traumatic in magnitude, may result in desirable growth and the strengthening of bone.[2]

The carpal index is used to determine the degree of ossification that has occurred at a given age, thereby indicating the extent of bony growth or development. The carpal index utilizes X rays of the wrist bones (the carpals) in order to determine skeletal age in relation to chronological age.

Bones grow in width by adding new bone tissue at their outer

[1] Arthur Steindler, *Kinesiology of the Human Body* (Springfield, Ill.: Charles C Thomas, Publisher, 1955), pp. 5–10.
[2] D. Mainland, *Anatomy as a Basis for Medical and Dental Practice* (New York: Harper & Row, Publishers, 1945), pp. 80–84.

edges beneath the periosteum. This process is analogous to tree growth. The long bones of the arms and legs grow near the ends, where a strip of cartilage remains throughout the growing years. The long bones, as well as the new bones, grow rapidly during puberty but do not become firmly united until several years later. A description of the bone segments involved in long-bone growth includes (1) the shaft of the long bone, called the *diaphysis;* (2) at either end of the shaft, the area of bone growth called the *metaphysis;* (3) immediately beyond the ends of the metaphyses, a cartilage called the *epiphyseal plate;* (4) a body structure separated from the shaft by the cartilage and called the *epiphysis.* Bone growth occurs at the epiphysis and the metaphysis. When the epiphysis and the diaphysis unite or become ossified into a single unit, growth in length ceases.

Development occurs at different rates for different parts of the body. It also occurs at different rates for the ages at which the various bones reach maturity. Some examples of the differences in skeletal maturity may help to clarify this principle. At birth, the human being has no epiphyses in the hand and he has no carpals. At about two years of age, two or three wrist bones appear. During the preschool years, epiphyses and most of the carpals appear. Not until adolescence does the last carpal bone appear. Union of the epiphyses and the carpals of the hand is not completed until approximately eighteen years of age. The hip bones do not unite until around twelve or fourteen years of age, whereas the sacral bones unite at about eighteen years. The spine at birth is soft, pliable, and easily distorted since it is basically cartilaginous in structure. Approximately one-half to two-thirds of the entire growth of the vertebrae occurs during the first three years, although the vertebrae continue to grow until the early twenties. A further example may be illustrated in the development of the adult curves of the spine. At birth, the spine is characterized by a single posterior or flexion curve. This initial flexion curve remains in the thoracic and sacral-coccygeal areas of the spine. The anterior or hyperextension curve of the cervical spine appears when the child becomes able to raise his head. The anterior or hyperextension curve of the lumbar spine comes from kicking and walking, because of the pull of the spinal extensors. The thoracic curve becomes more pronounced when the child is able to manipulate his hands in front of him.

POSTURAL CHARACTERISTICS OF DIFFERENT
DEVELOPMENTAL LEVELS

Each developmental level has its own characteristic traits. The relationship of various developmental levels to postural patterns is of particular interest to the physical educator. One can readily observe that children of different ages evince different standing positions and walking patterns. Nonetheless, the postural conditions of young children are frequently evaluated by standards that are usually based on the adult structure. Therefore, it would appear essential that the physical educator have a thorough understanding of the postural characteristics of the various growth and developmental stages through which the child will pass in striving for maturity. The results of such a study might eliminate the confusion of mistaking the characteristics of a particular developmental period for postural defects. Some of these characteristics are normal at one developmental level; they may become postural defects at a subsequent period in the child's development.

Most children are born with supinated feet (soles of the feet turned inward), bowlegs, internal tibial torsion (longitudinal twisting of the tibia) and muscular imbalance of the knees, hips, and trunk. These characteristics probably result in some degree from the fetal position. In this position, the trunk is flexed upon the hip, and the hips are rotated outward with the knees flexed. In addition, the soles of the feet are turned inward. Therefore, due to the intrauterine pressure on the flexors of these body segments, these muscles may be shorter in relation to the extensors. However, as the child begins weight bearing, or standing, in the early stages of walking, he will evidence some degree of pronation (weight bearing on the medial border of the foot while the sole of the foot is turned slightly outward) and knock-knees. As a consequence of assuming the standing position, greater pressure—gravity exerting its effect on the body—is applied to the lateral borders of the feet and knees. This pressure, in accordance with Wolff's law, stimulates bone growth on the lateral border of the foot, resulting in a normal growth pattern. This developmental process continues until about the age of three. There is a gradual decrease until about six years of age, at which time the lateral deviation of the knees and the internal torsion of the tibia have practically disappeared. In addition, the degree of pronation has lessened considerably.

The posture of the preschool child is characterized by a prominent abdomen, an exaggeration of the lumbar curve, a relatively straight back, and prominent or protruding scapulae (winged scapulae). The prominent abdomen results in part from the downward pull of gravity upon the abdominal viscera. The abdominal musculature of the preschool child is relatively weak. Because of the downward pull of the flexors of the hip and the associated weakness of the abdominal muscles, the anterior aspect of the pelvis is pulled down, causing an increase of the lumbar curve. The scapulae are prominent because of the slow development of the serratus anterior, which plays an important role in holding the scapulae to the rib cage. Another factor contributing to this condition is that the rib cage is rounded, and inclined downward from the pull of the abdominal muscles. Therefore, the ribs do not present a surface that is well suited to receive the scapulae.

By the time the average child enters school, he usually no longer has knock-knees. The pronation of the feet has practically disappeared. The child will, however, still have a somewhat prominent abdomen and its accompanying increased lumbar curve. He may assume an extended position of the knees while standing, but when walking or running he will still be unable fully to extend his knees and hips, and will evidence the tendency to flex the knees and hips slightly. This tendency toward flexion of the hip and knees persists because the flexors of the hip are stronger than the extensors of the hip, which are gaining in strength. His head, neck and shoulders will be in good alignment, but he may appear to have an increase in the thoracic curve. This apparent increase is caused by the sunken appearance of the chest as a result of the downward displacement of the rib cage.

The posture of preadolescence is somewhat different from that of the earlier developmental periods. It is characterized by a straight upper back, straight neck, aligned shoulders, and depressed chest. The abdomen may be prominent, but the degree of increase in the lumbar curve is considerably less than in the earlier periods. From the standpoint of body alignment, the preadolescent is approaching the adult standard for the first time. Evidence of specific body type is more pronounced. Typically, he is extremely active, and his activity is very general, which may account in part for his "good" posture at this time.

The posture of the adolescent is extremely difficult to describe, since it encompasses a period from twelve to twenty years of age. However, from fourteen to seventeen years of age, body type becomes firmly established. At this time, the adolescent's posture is characteristic of that of his adult life. One must remember, however, that this is a period of rapid growth. The individual often assumes positions that may cause temporary postural deviations or may lead to permanent postural habits. In two examples of such adaptations, (1) girls may become extremely self-conscious about the development of their breasts; consequently, they may assume a forward- or round-shoulder position in order to conceal or minimize their bust size; and (2) the tall adolescent may assume a slouch position to conform more closely to the size of his peers, and thus increase his thoracic curve.

In sum, consideration of the factors affecting growth and development is a challenge to the physical educator if he is to plan and conduct a scientifically sound program of physical education. Through his continual observation and study, he can determine those students that need to be referred to appropriate medical personnel. The physician should provide adequate guidance in determining the normalcy or abnormality of the structure or function observed.

Selected References

Breckenridge, Marian E., *Child Development,* 4th ed. Philadelphia: W. B. Saunders Co., 1960.

Britten, Samuel D., "A Unit of Work in Growth and Development and Early Detection of Physical Divergencies of the Elementary School Child." Paper presented to the Joint Conference of the Southwest District, American Association for Health, Physical Education and Recreation, and California Association for Health, Physical Education and Recreation, Long Beach, California, 1963.

Curriculum Committee for Health, Physical Education, and Safety in the Elementary Schools, "Child Growth and Development, Characteristics and Needs," *Journal of the American Association for Health, Physical Education and Recreation,* XX (April 1949).

Davies, Evelyn A., *The Elementary School Child and His Posture Patterns*. New York: Appleton-Century-Crofts, Inc., 1958.

Garrison, Karl C., *Growth and Development*, 2nd ed. New York: David McKay Co., Inc., 1959.

Hurlock, Elizabeth B., *Adolescent Development*, 3rd ed. New York: McGraw-Hill Book Co., Inc., 1956.

Knipping, H. W., "Sports in Medicine," in *Therapeutic Exercise*, ed. Sidney Licht. New Haven, Conn.: Elizabeth Licht, 1958.

Lee, J. Murray, and Dorris May Lee, *The Child and His Development*. New York: Appleton-Century-Crofts, Inc., 1958.

Mathews, Donald K., Robert Kruse, and Virginia Shaw, *The Science of Physical Education for Handicapped Children*. New York: Harper & Row, Publishers, 1962.

Rarick, G. Lawrence, "Exercise and Growth," in *Science and Medicine of Exercise and Sports*, ed. W. R. Johnson. New York: Harper & Row, Publishers, 1960.

Steindler, Arthur, *Kinesiology of the Human Body*. Springfield, Ill.: Charles C Thomas, Publisher, 1955.

Thorpe, Louis P., and Wendell W. Cruze, *Developmental Psychology*. New York: Ronald Press Co., 1956.

5

MUSCULOSKELETAL MAN

Man's overt movement is a result of complex interrelationships within his musculoskeletal system. In order to provide a basis upon which adaptations of muscular activity can be established, this chapter will discuss from a general viewpoint the fundamental operation of the muscles and bones. In Chapter 6, specific attention will be paid to anatomical structures and their functional components that are deemed important to the study of adapted physical education.

MUSCULOSKELETAL SYSTEM

Joint Structure

Movement of the human body takes place at the junctions or articulations of the bones of the skeleton. A joint, which is a result of these articulations between two or more bones, may be classified in three ways: (a) immovable, (b) slightly movable, and (c) freely movable. An example of an immovable articulation is the junction formed at the sutures of the skull. An example of the second classification, the slightly movable joint, exists at the symphysis pubis. The third type is seen in most of the large joints of the extremities.

Since the student of adapted physical education is mainly concerned with freely movable joints, emphasis here is placed upon the knowledge of such joints. Joints are held together by ligaments, variously arranged fibrous tissues, tendons, and muscles. In the freely movable joint, a ligamentous housing surrounds the articulation and is known as the *articular capsule*. This capsule is lined with a synovial membrane which secretes a lubricant known as *synovial fluid*. On the ends of the surfaces where the bones come together and make contact with each other, a cartilage is located to provide a smooth operational surface. It is called the *articular cartilage*. In some joints—the knee, for example—an additional piece of cartilage lies between the articular cartilages of the tibia and the femur. Some other joints also have *interarticular discs*. Freely movable joints are further described as (1) gliding, (2) hinge, (3) ball and socket, (4) pivot, (5) condyloid, and (6) saddle.

A functional distinction should be made between ligaments and tendons. Even though their basic structures are similar from a microscopic standpoint, the arrangement of fibers and other factors cause them to differ. Fundamentally, ligaments attach bone to bone, whereas tendons serve to attach muscle to bone and muscle to skin. Tendons may also have other anatomical relationships. But, in order to make a functional distinction between ligaments and tendons, one should regard a tendon as a functional extension of a muscle—as a fibrous structure that connects the muscle to other structures, particularly to bone. The tendon often provides a narrowed attachment for the muscle, thereby preventing large, bulky muscle masses from having to function at joints. For example, if the muscle belly instead of the tendon were to cross the wrist joint, it is unlikely that such a highly skilled mechanism as the hand would exist. Tendons provide certain pulley actions that allow greater efficiency, especially where fine movements are desired. In addition to these functional differences, ligaments are nonelastic and do not shorten adaptively. Muscle tissue will adapt in length to habitually shortened positions if enough time is allowed for it to do so. In the case of poliomyelitis, when the *agonist* has lost its innervation, the tendon of the *antagonist*—because of its ability to shorten by active contraction—will eventually adapt to its shortest length if proper therapeutic exercise is not employed to maintain an adequate range of motion. Understanding the differences between ligaments and tendons is of major importance to the physical educator.

The integrity of joints, especially those of the limbs, is maintained by the surrounding structures. The ligaments serve as limiting factors to extremes and directions of motion of the bones. The articular capsule functions as a support or "housing," and the tendons and their associated muscles provide movement as well as support and stability of the joint. Of these structures, the muscles and their tendinous attachments are the major stabilizing components of the joints. In subsequent chapters, we will see that the restabilization of joint motion after injury is one of the more important functions of therapeutic exercise.

Not only do ligaments function as limiting components for extremes in range of motion, but the location of the ligaments at each joint largely determines the type of movement that the muscles can provide. Of course, other factors, such as the shape of the articulating bones, also help to determine the movement potential of each joint. In the elbow joint, the humerus articulates with the ulna in a hinge-like fashion. At the extreme of elbow extension, the olecranon process contacts the posterior surface of the distal end of the humerus in an action similar to that of a doorstop. Thus, acting in connection with ligaments, this structure limits hyperextension of the elbow in the normal individual. The ligaments along the sides of the joint prevent medial and lateral movement of the distal end of the ulna. In addition to ligaments, bony formations at the joints must be considered in relation to the movements which are possible at joints. The hinge-like relationship of the humerus and ulna at the elbow helps to predetermine the potential movement at that joint.

Spatial Relationship

If the limiting ligaments are on the medial and lateral sides of a joint and a muscle is attached anterior to the joint, one should expect, for example, only *flexion* of the elbow and only *extension* of the knee. The point is this: in order to understand the movement at joints from a functional viewpoint, it is necessary to know the *spatial relationship*—the position of the ligaments and muscles in relation to the joints.

Spatial relationship, in terms of muscle function, aids in the determination of muscle action. If a given joint permits flexion and extension only, then the muscles that cross the joint will in turn perform flexion or extension at that joint, depending upon the anatomical location of the muscles. There are a few rare exceptions. For instance, the abductor pollicis brevis muscle crosses the carpometacarpal joint and the metacarpophalangeal joint of the thumb. But, despite this muscle's being in a position to abduct at the metacarpophalangeal joint, it cannot abduct because the ligaments of the joint permit only flexion and extension. Along with some other minor movements, the major action of that muscle is abduction of the carpometacarpal joint of the thumb. In consequence, if one knows the movements that are possible at a joint, and the spatial relationship of the muscles to that joint, the major actions of the muscles will be obvious.

MUSCULATURE

The three basic types of muscle are (1) *involuntary,* or smooth; (2) *cardiac,* or heart; and (3) *voluntary,* or skeletal. There are histological differences among these types, but we shall be concerned mainly with the voluntary, or skeletal, muscle. Muscles perform various functions through their ability to contract, relax, and to stretch. Alternations between contraction and relaxation of skeletal muscles as they span joints and act upon the articulations of the bones result in movement.

Muscular Contraction

Contraction is identified with the development of *tension.* But tension, after being applied through a system of levers, can either overcome a resistance and result in shortening a muscle, or be overcome by a resistance and result in lengthening the muscle. In either case, the muscle is regarded as "contracting," or developing tension.

When muscles are functioning in a static state, they are in *isometric* contraction. When they are in movement or acting in phase with each other or performing *phasic* actions, they are in *isotonic* contraction. Since a movement that is phasic involves shortening or lengthening (isotonic contractions of the muscle), a further description of the actions is necessary. Therefore, the shortening of a muscle during isotonic contraction is called *concentric* contraction. The lengthening of a muscle during an isotonic contraction is called an *eccentric* contraction.

Volitional and Reflex Activity

The coordination of groups of muscles acting either with or against one another to effect a gross or a fine motor movement is a highly complex function. Detailed neurophysiological discussions may be found in basic texts on the subject. The purpose of introducing this topic here is to call attention to the important role of various reflex operations within the human organism. Basic reflexes that are not generally seen in the normal individual are often exhibited very clearly in some neurological disorders. Therefore, a general understanding of simple reflexes will help clarify descriptions of certain disorders that are considered in later chapters.

Controlled voluntary movements come from combinations of simple reflexes that are modulated by the higher centers of the brain and by complex feedback from the active peripheral parts. The results are smooth, coordinated movements having little resemblance to any one of the basic reflexes that went into making the movement. The neuromuscular system of the human organism is a self-regulating system that operates similarly to electronic servo machines.[1] These machines have the built-in ability to repair or reregulate themselves if needed. In the human, the muscle *spindle* plays an important role of autoregulation. Muscle spindles, containing small muscle fibers and neurons, exist throughout the muscle. The spindles function in such a way that they generate signals

---

[1] Norbert Wiener, *The Human Use of Human Beings,* 2nd ed., rev. (New York: Doubleday & Co., Inc., 1954).

to keep the nervous system continuously aware of the length and tension of the muscle. To help shed some light on the operation of the neuromuscular system, an introduction to reflex action follows.

A reflex may be defined as an involuntary act. *Reflex arcs* or loops are formed through a *synapse, or* connection, between a sensory, or *afferent,* neuron and a motor, or *efferent,* neuron. A neuron consists of a nerve-cell body and all its processes. There are five basic parts to the reflex arc: (1) receptor organ, (2) afferent fiber, (3) synapse, (4) efferent fiber, and (5) effector organ.

Although many classifications exist physiologically, reflexes are generally categorized as (a) *interoceptive*—arising from the viscera; (b) *exteroceptive*—arising from the body surface sense organs; and (c) *proprioceptive*—arising in joints, muscles, tendons, labyrinths of the inner ear, the neck, and the eyes.

Perhaps the simplest reflex upon which movement is based is the *postural* or *spinal* reflex. No central-nervous-system level higher than the spinal cord need be involved. This reflex functions to maintain the body in an antigravity position—to resist reflexly the pull of gravity without the individual necessarily being aware of the reflex action. The pull of gravity exerts a downward force on the body. When the person is standing, sense receptors in the tendon of the extensor muscles respond to this force. These receptors in turn *synapse* (connect) with lower motor neurons in the spinal cord. A motor impulse sent via neuroanatomical paths activates the motor unit in the quadriceps. The motor unit, which is a part of this basic reflex arc, responds on an all-or-none basis. The muscle fibers of the motor unit will contract (perhaps two to three hundred fibers in the quadriceps) and many other motor units will be activated. The number depends upon the amount of contraction needed. Thus, *stretch* in an antigravity extensor muscle automatically results in the contraction of that muscle. An example of one stretch reflex is the knee jerk: with the knees crossed in the sitting position, striking the quadriceps tendon will produce an automatic kick of the lower leg.

The *flexion* or *withdrawal* reflex is of importance in any consideration of basic reflexes in movement. This reflex is characterized by a complete withdrawal of a body part. For example, if the sole of the foot is forcefully stroked to cause a threshold of pain, the foot will dorsiflex and the knee and hip joints will also go into flexion.

In the postural reflex, mentioned previously, stimulation of the extensor muscles results in contraction of those muscles. This contraction is often termed the *extensor* reflex or the *extensor thrust* reflex.

A smooth, coordinated, reciprocal combination of the flexor and extensor reflexes constitutes the main basis of locomotion. When these reflexes function alternately and in combination with each other in the limbs, they are referred to as the *crossed extensor* reflex.

The existence of an over-all state of muscular activity appears to be present no matter how much relaxation can be achieved by the individual. The phenomenon known as *muscle tonus* is not clearly understood. Muscle tonus may be defined as low-level muscular activity resulting from changes in tension that cause the motor units to fire alternately. It has been hypothesized that muscle tonus provides the muscle with a state of readiness to help in counteracting sudden changes in position due to gravitational and other forces.

Joint and Muscle Interrelationships

In any consideration of musculoskeletal relationships, certain kinesiophysiological applications should be noted. When determining the optimum point at which muscles can exert their greatest force at a given joint, at least three elements will be involved: (1) the angle of the joint, (2) the angle of the pull of the muscle to the bony lever, and (3) the length of the muscle at the time the force is to be exerted. Because of limitations in our present knowledge, however, it is not possible to indicate, for instance, the specific point at which such a factor as strength development might best be attained. Although investigators have made determinations of the points at which strength is maximum for groups of experimental subjects, it is known that individuals who participate in specific kinds of activities other than those participated in by the general population have greater strength at other points in the range of motion than those indicated in the research literature.

Selected References

Cooper, John M., and Ruth B. Glassow, *Kinesiology*. St. Louis: C. V. Mosby Co., 1963.

Davis, Elwood C., and Gene A. Logan, *Biophysical Values of Muscular Activity*. Dubuque, Iowa: Wm. C. Brown Co., 1961.

Fulton, John F., ed., *A Textbook of Physiology*, 17th ed. Philadelphia: W. B. Saunders Co., 1955.

Gray, Henry, *Anatomy of the Human Body*, ed. Charles M. Goss, 27th ed. Philadelphia: Lea & Febiger, 1959.

Riedman, Sarah R., *Physiology of Work and Play*. New York: Holt, Rinehart and Winston, Inc., 1950.

Wells, Katharine F., *Kinesiology*, 3rd ed. Philadelphia: W. B. Saunders Co., 1960.

6

MUSCULOSKELETAL MOVEMENT

Anatomists long ago developed a complex system with which movement of the body could be discussed in a standardized fashion. As a result, a common language now exists. This system was based on the use of planes and axes of motion, and the *anatomical position* is the basic reference or starting point for utilizing the descriptive terminology that is based upon such planes and axes of motion. In this position, the body is erect with the arms at the sides, and the palms of the hands are facing forward. Originally, this position may have been one in which cadavers were placed so that anatomists could work most effectively when dissecting.

It is necessary to define an anatomical position to serve as a standard reference for defining and naming joint actions. Once a given joint action has been named and defined, then the joint-action terminology suffices even if the body position is changed and other joints have been moved out of anatomical position. Difficulty arises, however, in attempting to apply this formalized terminology when one begins to describe basic movement patterns. The body very rarely moves in those planes that the anatomists employ for description. An analysis of most movements reveals that the human organism functions in diagonal patterns of motion.

ANATOMICAL MOVEMENTS

Attempts have been made to describe diagonal movements by beginning with references drawn from traditional "cold cut" anatomical descriptive terminology. An adequate terminology for describing gross movement patterns does not exist for the physical educator.

Spatial relationship of muscles to joints was discussed in the previous chapter. According to that discussion, if the movements, flexion and extension for example, are the only movements possible at a given joint, and the muscle or muscles spanning the joint attach in such a manner that flexion or extension will occur, then the action of the muscle can be deduced. With this in mind, very little mention of the action of muscles will be considered here. What will be emphasized is a knowledge of (a) the movements possible at joints, (b) the bones and ligaments that make up those joints, and (c) the muscles with their tendons which cross the joints. These fundamentals are essential for adaptations of muscular activity in the form of therapeutic exercise.

In defining anatomical movements, the assumption is made here that the body is in the anatomical position and that the definitions pertain only to the beginning of the movement in order to describe the *direction* of motion. For example, if from the anatomical position the upper arm is moved in the frontal plane away from the midline of the body, the action at the shoulder joint is called *abduction*. If this same movement is continued for more than 90 degrees, the upper arm will then be moving back *toward* the midline of the body. But since this movement beyond 90 degrees is purely a continuation of the initial movement away from the center line of the body, it is still called abduction.

Anatomical positions and movements with their definitions are contained in the following list:[1]

1. *Abduction*—movement away from the midline of the body.
2. *Adduction*—movement toward the midline of the body.
3. *Circumduction*—movement of a limb in a manner that describes a cone.

---

1 Gene A. Logan et al., *Student Handbook for Adapted Physical Education* (Dubuque, Iowa: Wm. C. Brown Co., 1960), p. 6.

4. *Depression*—downward movement of a part.

5. *Dorsiflexion*—bending foot upward (flexion of the ankle).

6. *Elevation*—upward movement of a part.

7. *Eversion*—movement of the sole of the foot outward.

8. *Extension*—movement resulting in the increase of a joint angle.

9. *Flexion*—movement resulting in a decrease of a joint angle.

10. *Horizontal abduction*—movement of the arms from a front horizontal position to a side horizontal position.

11. *Horizontal adduction*—movement of the arms from a side horizontal position to a front horizontal position.

12. *Hyperextension*—movement beyond the position of extension.

13. *Inversion*—movement of the sole of the foot inward.

14. *Lateral flexion*—movement of the trunk sideways from the midline of the body.

15. *Plantar flexion*—bending the foot downward (extension of the ankle).

16. *Pronation*—turning the back of the hand forward.

17. *Prone position*—lying in a face-down position.

18. *Protraction*—forward movement of a part (shoulder girdle).

19. *Retraction*—backward movement of a part (shoulder girdle).

20. *Rotation "downward"*—rotary movement of the scapula with the inferior angle moving medially and downward.

21. *Rotation medially*—movement around the axis of a bone toward the midline of the body.

22. *Rotation laterally*—movement around the axis of a bone away from the midline of the body.

23. *Rotation "upward"*—rotary movement of the scapula with the inferior angle moving laterally and upward.

24. *Supination*—turning the palm of the hand forward.

25. *Supine position*—lying in a face-up position.

MAJOR JOINTS AND THEIR MOVEMENTS

The following chart presents together (1) the major joints, (2) the classification of the joints, (3) the bones by which the joints are formed, and (4) the anatomical movements that are possible at these joints.

JOINT	TYPE	BONES INVOLVED	MOVEMENTS POSSIBLE
Ankle	Hinge	Tibia, fibula, talus	Dorsiflexion, plantar flexion
Knee	Modified hinge	Tibia, femur, patella	Flexion, extension, rotation (when knee is bent)
Hip	Ball and socket	Femur, pelvis	Flexion, extension, adduction, abduction, medial and lateral rotation, circumduction, hyperextension
Intervertebral (Spine)	Gliding	Vertebrae	Flexion, extension, rotation, lateral flexion
Shoulder	Ball and socket	Humerus, scapula	Flexion, extension, adduction, abduction, medial and lateral rotation, circumduction, hyperextension, horizontal adduction, horizontal abduction
Sternoclavicular (shoulder girdle)	Gliding	Clavicle, sternum, scapula	Elevation, depression, protraction, retraction, rotation, circumduction
Acromioclavicular (scapula)	Gliding	Scapula, clavicle	Elevation, depression, adduction, abduction, "upward" and "downward" rotation
Elbow	Hinge	Humerus, radius, ulna	Flexion, extension
Radioulnar	Pivot	Radius, ulna	Pronation, supination
Wrist	Condyloid	Radius, navicular, lunate, triangular	Flexion, extension, adduction, abduction, circumduction (adduction and abduction also called ulnar and radial deviation)
First carpometacarpal (thumb)	Saddle	Multangular, first metacarpal	Flexion, extension, adduction, abduction, circumduction

KINESIOANATOMICAL STRUCTURES AND RELATIONSHIPS

Many anatomical structures and functions of the body are more vulnerable to negative adaptive changes than others. Some areas seem to be especially susceptible to injury—perhaps because of weaknesses or because of undue stresses placed upon them in specific physical activities. Disabling conditions tend to have similar effects upon most individuals involved with those conditions. Therefore, certain recurring problems will be encountered.

It seems appropriate to highlight those kinesioanatomical relationships that must be understood in order to adapt muscular activity to individuals with disabling conditions. Since not all anatomical structures can be presented here, those structures that are most frequently involved in disabilities will receive the greatest consideration. Maximum attention will be paid also to the major joints of the limbs. Surveys of students served by adapted physical education programs indicate that there is a high incidence of disabilities in these areas.[2]

The manner in which each illustration of kinesioanatomical structures is shown is somewhat different from the usual presentation. Only alphabetical letters are used to indicate the important elements. Nomenclature and descriptive information for each illustration is in the text near it. Most of these illustrations have been utilized for instructional purposes in a different form for a number of years.[3]

Only a brief presentation is made for each illustration in the following kinesioanatomical discussion. This section is intended as a source of basic material. Contained herein will be anatomical structures with kinesiological considerations which have a specific application to the adaptations of muscular activity for individuals with physical disabilities. The ankle, foot, knee, hip, trunk, shoulder, shoulder girdle, and elbow will be presented.

[2] James G. Dunkelberg and Gene A. Logan, "Let the Doctor Recommend Adapted Physical Education," *Journal of the Association for Health, Physical Education and Recreation,* XXIX, No. 5 (June 1958), 28.

[3] Gene A. Logan, "Instructional Slides for Athletic Training and Rehabilitation" (Springfield, Mo.: Box 3535 Glenstone Station).

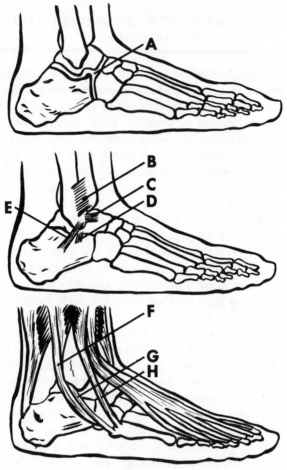

Figure 6.1

Side-to-side motion of eversion and inversion of the ankle takes place at the transverse tarsal joint. The heavy line in Figure 6.1 at A indicates the articulations that form this joint. Plantar flexion and dorsiflexion are the only motions that take place in the normal ankle joint. The lateral or side-to-side motion that appears to take place in the ankle joint actually occurs below the talus bone. The major ligaments of the ankle are shown from a lateral view: B, anterior tibiofibular; C, anterior talofibular; D, lateral talocalcaneal;

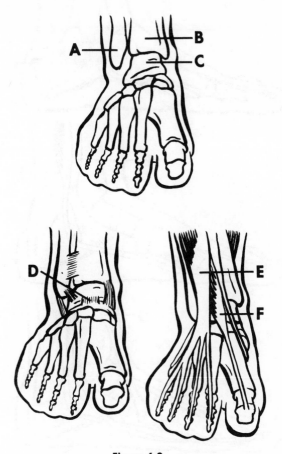

Figure 6.2

and E, calcaneofibular. The lateral stabilizing muscles are indicated
F, peroneus longus; G, peroneus brevis; and H, peroneus tertius.

The bony structures of the ankle viewed from the front are
shown in Figure 6.2. Three bones compose the ankle joint: A,
fibula; B, tibia; and C, talus. Only one ligament is noted in this
view: D, talonavicular. Anterior stabilizing muscles are pointed out:
E, extensor digitorum longus; F, extensor hallucis longus.

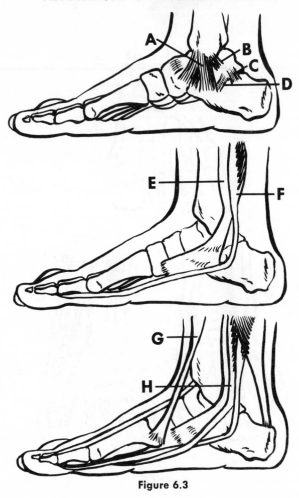

Figure 6.3

Medial and posterior ligaments are indicated in Figure 6.3: A, deltoid; B, posterior talotibial; C, posterior talocalcaneal; D, medial talocalcaneal. Of these ligaments, the deltoid is the strongest and most important. Often, when extreme stresses are placed upon this ligament, chip fractures of the tibia occur since the ligament has such great tensile strength. Medial stabilizing muscles of the ankle are shown: E, tibialis posterior; F, flexor hallucis longus; G, tibialis anterior; H, flexor digitorum longus. These muscles, in

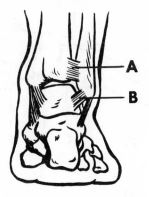

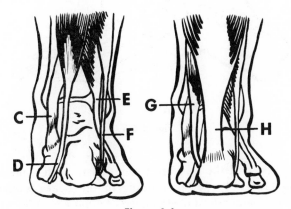

Figure 6.4

addition to their stabilizing components of the ankle on the medial side, also serve to help support the longitudinal arch.

Posterior ligaments of the ankle are shown in Figure 6.4: A, posterior tibiofibular; B, posterior talofibular. Medial stabilizing muscles of the ankle are shown from the rear: C, tibialis posterior; D, flexor hallucis longus; G, flexor digitorum longus. Lateral stabilizing muscles are also shown from a posterior view: E, peroneus brevis; F, peroneus longus. The tendon of the gastrocnemius-soleus muscle group sometimes called the triceps surae is indicated: H, Achilles tendon.

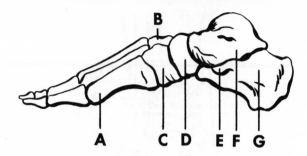

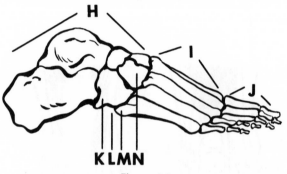

Figure 6.5

The bones of the foot are structured in such a manner that they form arches. Proper positioning of the bones is maintained primarily by ligaments and secondarily by muscles. Weight is born by the calcaneus and the metatarsal heads. The bones and important landmarks of the feet are represented in Figure 6.5 from medial as well as lateral views: A, first metatarsal; B, second cuneiform; C, first cuneiform; D, navicular; E, sustentaculum tali of the calcaneus; F, talus; G, calcaneus; H, tarsals; I, metatarsals; J, phalanges; K, cuboid; L, groove for the peroneus longus muscle; M, fifth metatarsal; N, third cuneiform.

In Figure 6.6, deep structures that help to maintain the medial longitudinal arch are the calcaneonavicular or "spring" ligament (A) and the sustentaculum tali (bony projection from the calcaneus), which, in turn, is supported by the tendon of the flexor hallucis longus (C). The "spring" ligament is one of the few ligaments

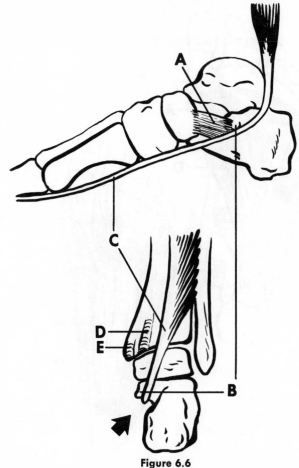

Figure 6.6

in the body that contain elastic fibers. It serves as a kind of elastic spring upon which rests the head of the talus bone. This ligament is often involved in the "falling" of the long arch, especially when the supporting muscles become weakened due to disuse. Pain is often noted at the site of this ligament. The reader should observe the direction of pull on the tendon of the flexor hallucis longus muscle indicated by the arrow. This muscle helps maintain the calcaneus in an upright position and aids in correct positioning of the bones that compose the arch of the foot.

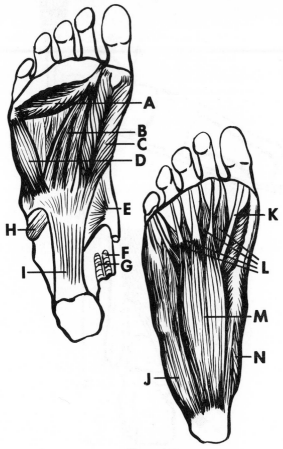

Figure 6.7

Some of the structures of the sole of the foot are indicated in Figure 6.7. Beneath most of the muscles on the posterior plantar surface of the foot is the long plantar ligament (I). Some of the short muscles of the foot which comprise the third layer are indicated: A and B, adductor hallucis; C, flexor hallucis brevis; D, flexor digiti minimi. Note the large area (five bones) covered by the tendon of the tibialis posterior (E). The flexor digitorum longus and the flexor hallucis longus tendons ride in the grooves (F) and (G). Other important muscles of the foot are shown: H, peroneus

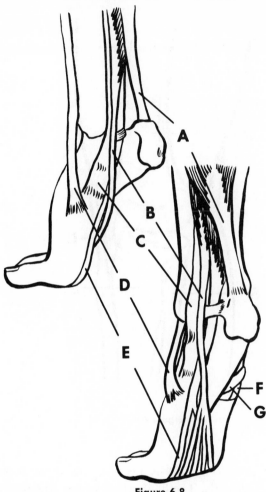

Figure 6.8

longus tendon; J, abductor digiti minimi; K, flexor hallucis longus; L, lumbricales; M, flexor digitorum brevis; N, abductor hallucis.

Some of the same muscles indicated in Figure 6.7 are also shown in another view in Figure 6.8. Tendons of the long muscles which move, stabilize, and support this area are indicated. A, Achilles tendon; B, flexor digitorum longus; C, tibialis posterior; D, tibialis anterior; E, flexor hallucis longus; F, peroneus brevis; G, peroneus longus.

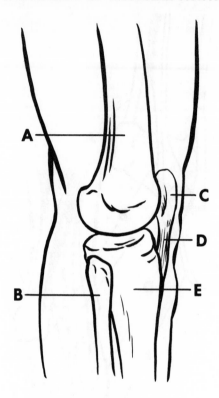

Figure 6.9

The knee joint (Fig. 6.9) is made up of three bones: A, femur; E, tibia; C, patella. The fibula (B) does not articulate at the knee joint. The patellar ligament (D), running from bone to bone in this case, is actually the tendon of the quadriceps muscle group that attaches to the tibial tuberosity.

The right knee joint flexed to 90 degrees and viewed anteriorly is shown in Figure 6.10: A, lateral collateral ligament; B, meniscus or semilunar cartilage, or interarticular disc; C, tendon of the biceps femoris (cut); D, posterior cruciate ligament; E, anterior cruciate ligament; F, medial collateral ligament. The main function of the ligaments indicated at D and E is to prevent excessive hy-

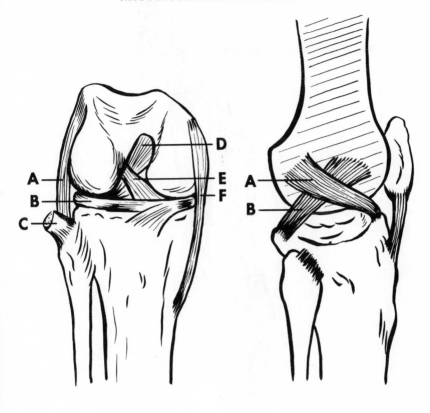

Figure 6.10   **Figure 6.11**

perextension and hyperflexion. All of the ligaments involved in the knee joint help to prevent rotation at the joint when the knee is extended, or in a straight position.

The cruciate ligaments are diagrammatically indicated in Figure 6.11: A, anterior cruciate; B, posterior cruciate. In order to show the position of these ligaments, the femur has been sectioned anterioposteriorly. When the tibia is forced posteriorly on a fixed femur, the posterior cruciate ligament may be injured. An injury may occur to the anterior cruciate ligament when the tibia is forced anteriorly while the femur is fixed.

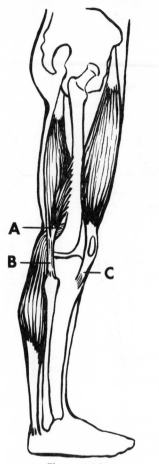

Figure 6.12

The general attachments of the three major muscles or muscle groups that act upon the knee joint are shown in Figure 6.12: A, gastrocnemius; B, hamstrings; C, quadriceps. These muscles are indicated diagrammatically so that the attachments may be easily visualized in terms of the functions of these muscles. Note that two major muscle groups attach below the joint and one major muscle group attaches above the joint. Strengthening these muscles for preventive or rehabilitative measures is one of the primary uses of therapeutic exercise.

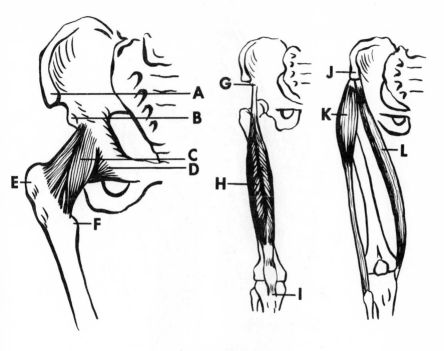

Figure 6.13

Anatomical structures that are related primarily to the hip and secondarily to the knee joint are presented in Figure 6.13. The hip joint is held intact by the iliofemoral or Y-ligament (C), and the pubofemoral ligament (D). Important structures in this area are indicated: A, anterior superior iliac spine; B, anterior inferior iliac spine; E, greater trochanter; F, lesser trochanter; G, proximal attachment of the rectus femoris (anterior inferior iliac spine); H, rectus femoris; I, distal attachment of the rectus femoris on the tibial tuberosity; J, proximal attachment—anterior superior iliac spine—tensor fasciae latae muscle; K, tensor fasciae latae; L, sartorius. The reader should note that the proximal attachment of the rectus femoris on the anterior inferior iliac spine is covered by the tensor fasciae latae and sartorius muscles, and it is not palpable in the normal individual.

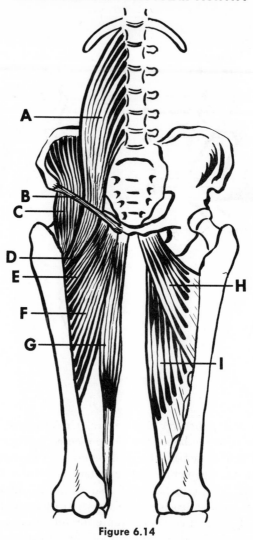

Figure 6.14

The major hip flexors and adductors are depicted in Figure 6.14. The inguinal ligament is also indicated. It serves in a kind of pulley arrangement to maintain functional positioning of the hip flexors. The adductor muscles of one hip are indicated on the right and left in the illustration. All of the muscles shown are actually located on one side or in one thigh and hip area only. They are separated here to illustrate their relative locations: A, psoas major;

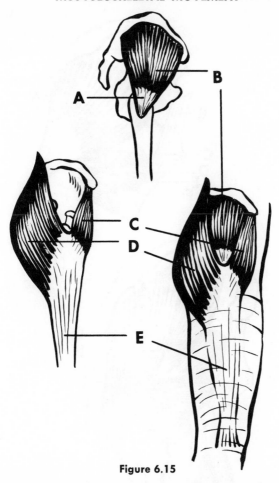

Figure 6.15

B, inguinal ligament; C, iliacus; D, attachment on lesser trochanter of iliopsoas group; E, pectineus; F, adductor longus; G, gracilis; H, adductor brevis; I, adductor magnus. Of the adductors shown, the gracilis is the only muscle that crosses the knee joint.

The hip is shown from the lateral side in Figure 6.15: attachment of the gluteus medius on the greater trochanter; B, location of the gluteus medius between the tensor fasciae latae (C) and the gluteus maximus (D); E, the tractus iliotibialis. It should be noted that the gluteus maximus, gluteus minimus, and the tensor fasciae latae form a group that functions similarly to the deltoid muscle of the shoulder.

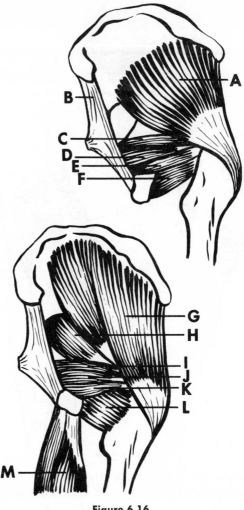

Figure 6.16

In Figure 6.16, the hip area is indicated from the back with the gluteus maximus removed: A, gluteus minimus; B, sacrotuberous ligament; C, gemellus superior; D, obturator internus; E, gemellus inferior; F, obturator externus; G, gluteus medius; H, piriformis; I, gemellus superior; J, obturator internus; K, gemellus inferior; L,

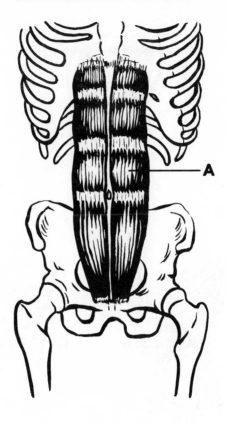

Figure 6.17

quadratus femoris (covering the obturator externus); M, hamstring group.

The rectus abdominis muscle is illustrated in Figure 6.17. This muscle (A), a trunk flexor that attaches to the rib cage and the pubis, is divided into separate segments by tendinous inscriptions. The muscle is also separated into a right and left rectus abdominis by the linea alba (white line). Deviation or curvature of this line is often an indication of a postural deformity of the trunk involving the spinal column.

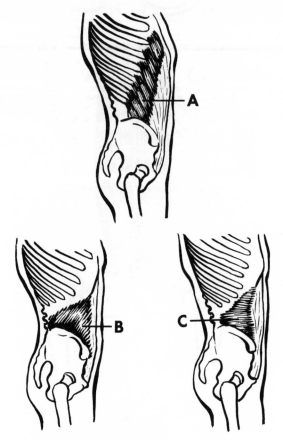

Figure 6.18

The muscles of the abdominal area, other than the rectus abdominis, are indicated in Figure 6.18: A, external oblique; B, internal oblique; C, transverse abdominis. These three muscles are
in layers. The external oblique is the most superficial and the transverse abdominis is the deepest of the three abdominal muscles. The
external oblique runs diagonally downward from lateral to medial
(the same direction as the fingers would run if the hands were
placed in the pockets). The external oblique on one side continues
into the internal oblique on the other side, forming a functional
unit. These two units form the shape of an "X." This design provides the muscles with the ability to work in conjunction with each

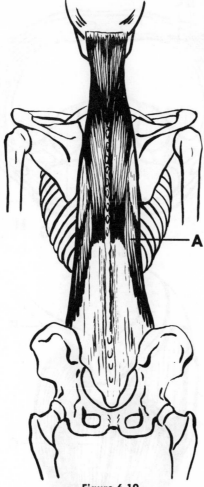

Figure 6.19

other for spine flexion and in opposition to each other for spine rotation and lateral flexion.

The longest muscle group in the body is represented in Figure 6.19. The spine extensor group (A), which begins at its attachment on the sacrum and pelvis and ends at the inferior nuchal line of the skull, is illustrated. This muscle group has four divisions. Each of these divisions is subdivided. The spine extensor group of muscles should be looked upon as a unit when its main functions, those of extension and hyperextension, are considered.

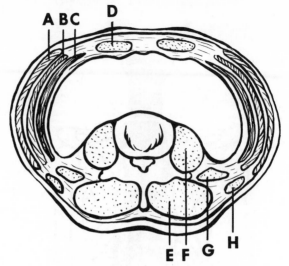

Figure 6.20

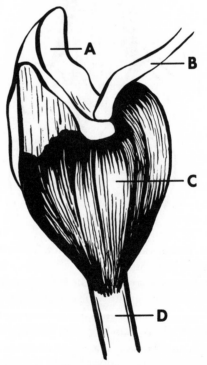

Figure 6.21

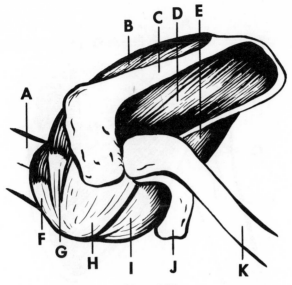

Figure 6.22

A cross-section of the trunk through the lumbar region is represented in Figure 6.20. The muscles passing through this level of the lumbar region are indicated: A, external oblique; B, internal oblique; C, transverse abdominis; D, rectus abdominis; E, erector spinae; F, psoas major; G, quadratus lumborum; H, latissimus dorsi. The reader should note the relationship that the erector spinae and psoas major have to the lumbar vertebra. A discussion of the functions of these muscles as they relate to normal and abnormal lumbar curvature will appear in Chapter 8.

The bony structure of the shoulder is indicated in Figure 6.21: A, scapula; B, clavicle; D, humerus. This view is from the side and slightly above the shoulder. The deltoid muscle is indicated (C).

The shoulder is viewed from above in Figure 6.22. The muscles and bones are shown with the deltoid muscle removed. The deep muscles surrounding and attaching to the humerus are also indicated: A, humerus; B, infraspinatus; C, spine of the scapula; D, supraspinatus; E, subscapularis; F, tendon of the teres minor; G, tendon of the infraspinatus; H, tendon of the supraspinatus; I, tendon of the subscapularis; J, coracoid process; K, clavicle. The four tendons indicated at F, G, H, and I make up the "rotary cuff." One

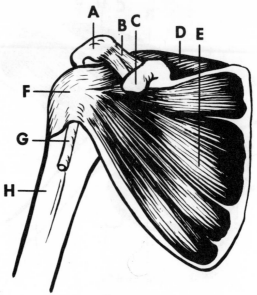

Figure 6.23

function of the "rotary cuff" is to maintain the head of the humerus in the glenoid fossa of the scapula. Another major function is to prevent the head of the humerus from jamming into the rooflike structure composed of the acromion process and the clavicle just above the head of the humerus.[4] This action occurs when the humerus is abducted or flexed at the shoulder joint.

The scapula and the humerus are shown in Figure 6.23 along with the deep structures which cross the shoulder joint. An anterior view of the "rotary cuff" is shown also. The following structures are represented: A, acromion process; B, coraco-acromial ligament; C, coracoid process; D, supraspinatus; E, subscapularis; F, "rotary cuff"; G, tendon (cut) of the long head of the biceps; H, humerus. Stability of the shoulder joint is largely dependent upon the functional integrity and strength of the subscapularis muscle. Along with the "rotary cuff," the coraco-acromial ligament serves as a pulley for the supraspinatus which, in turn, helps to prevent the humerus from jamming into the bony roof above the shoulder joint.

4 V. T. Inman et al., "Observations on the Function of the Shoulder Joint," *Journal of Bone and Joint Surgery*, XXVI, No. 1 (January 1944), 1–30.

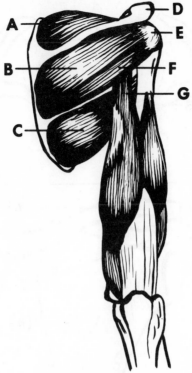

Figure 6.24

Attention is called to the coracoid process (C). Three muscles involved at this area of the shoulder attach to this bony process: (1) coracobrachialis, (2) short head of the biceps, and (3) pectoralis minor.

The deep muscles of the shoulder and upper arm are shown from a posterior view in Figure 6.24. These muscular relationships are indicated: A, supraspinatus; B, infraspinatus; C, teres major; D, acromion process; E, "rotary cuff"; F, teres minor; G, long head of the triceps. It should be observed that the long head of the triceps runs between the teres major and the teres minor to reach its attachment on the scapula. In addition, it should be noted that the teres minor is on the posterior surface of the humerus, and that the teres major is on the anterior surface. The long head of the triceps (G) is often involved in injuries, particularly from throwing movements, because of a lack of extensibility of this muscle.

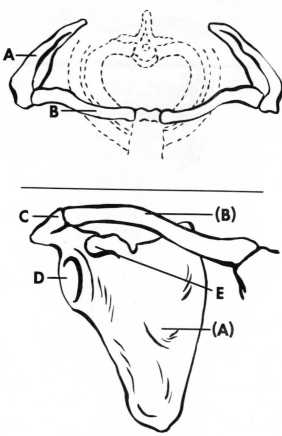

Figure 6.25

The shoulder girdle is viewed from above and from the front in Figure 6.25. The scapula (A) and the clavicle (B) are shown. Specific parts of the scapula are indicated: C, acromion process; D, glenoid fossa; E, coracoid process. The shoulder girdle is not a complete bony girdle like that found in the pelvis, but it does girdle the rib cage. The shoulder girdle is attached to the spinal column by way of the rhomboid muscles.

Muscles that bring about movement of the scapula are indicated in Figure 6.26. The important muscles are represented: A, rhomboid minor; B, rhomboid major; C, levator scapulae; D, ser-

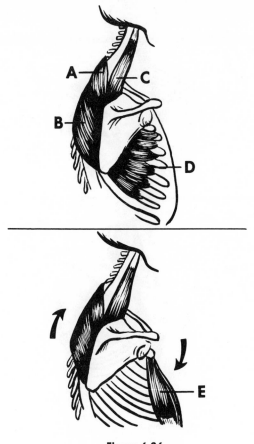

Figure 6.26

ratus anterior. Shortening of the rhomboids, levator scapulae, and the pectoralis minor muscles results in downward rotation of the scapula as indicated by the arrows. The pectoralis minor is indicated (E). Downward and upward rotary movements of the scapula are not true rotary movements because the point about which they revolve tends to move as the scapular movement is accomplished. Using the inferior angle of the scapula as a landmark, *medial* and upward movements of this point occur in downward rotation, *lateral* and upward movements occur in upward rotation.

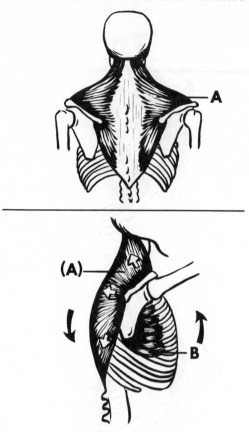

Figure 6.27

The illustrations in Figure 6.27 show the relationship between the trapezius and the serratus anterior muscles in performing the movement of upward rotation of the scapula. The two muscles are shown: A, trapezius; B, serratus anterior. The attachments of the trapezius along the spine of the scapula should be noted. Shortening of this muscle (indicated by small arrows) when the scapula is *adducted* brings about upward rotation of the scapula (large arrows). However, when the scapula is *abducted,* or moved away from the posterior midline of the body, upward rotation is performed primarily by the serratus anterior. The amount of movement performed by either one of these two muscles depends upon the position of the scapula in relation to the posterior midline of the body.

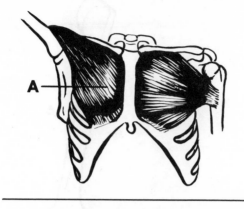

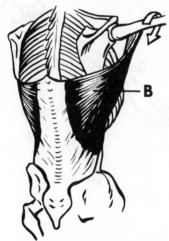

Figure 6.28

Figure 6.28 illustrates two muscles which are of great importance to the disabled person who must rely upon his upper limbs to perform such activities as crutch-walking. These two muscles are indicated: A, pectoralis major; B, latissimus dorsi. The arrow suggests the action of the latissimus dorsi. This muscle is an important medial rotator, adductor, and extensor of the humerus. Since the pectoralis major functions in a three-part relationship, several movements are possible. An understanding of the action of these two muscles is quite important in adaptations of muscular activity.

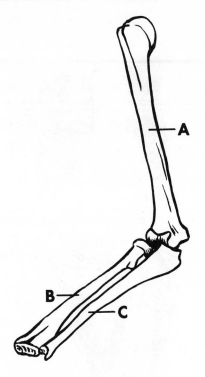

Figure 6.29

Bony structures of the right elbow are shown in Figure 6.29. The elbow joint is formed by these articulating bones: A, humerus; B, radius; C, ulna. Observe that the radius is wider at its distal end than is the ulna. The ulna forms the hinge joint with the humerus. When pronation (from a position of supination) is performed, the radius moves to a position diagonally across the ulna. In the anatomical position, it is parallel to the ulna.

Some of the muscles of the elbow joint are depicted in Figure 6.30. The brachialis muscle (A) attaches distally to the ulna. It is an

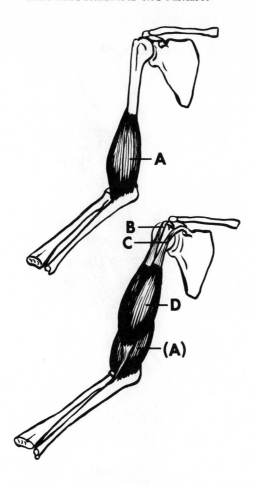

Figure 6.30

elbow flexor. Proximal tendons of the biceps, the long head (B) and
the short head (C), are pointed out. The muscle belly of the biceps
is indicated (D). Distally, the biceps tendon wraps around the radius
in order for the biceps to perform supination of the forearm. Flexion of the elbow, however, is the primary function of the biceps
muscle.

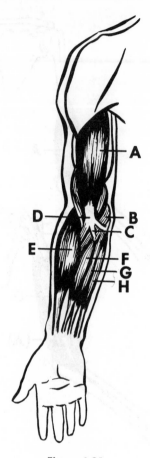

Figure 6.31

The superficial muscles anterior to the elbow joint are illustrated in Figure 6.31: A, biceps; B, pronator teres; C, lacertus fibrosus (tendinous slip from the distal biceps tendon); D, distal biceps tendon; E, brachioradialis; F, flexor carpi radialis; G, palmaris longus; H, flexor carpi ulnaris.

Posterior muscles acting upon the elbow joint are indicated in Figure 6.32: B, triceps; C, anconeus. These are the primary ex-

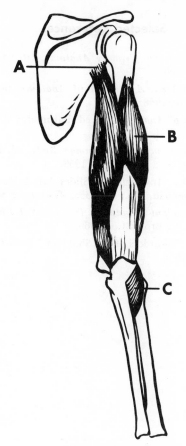

Figure 6.32

tensors of the elbow joint. The location of the long head of the triceps muscle is often neglected in the study of the function of this area. The long head of the triceps (A) attaches to the scapula just below the glenoid fossa. This muscle serves as an adductor and extensor at the shoulder joint. Its importance should not be overlooked in terms of adaptations of muscular activity, especially from the standpoint of therapeutic exercise.

Selected References

Basmajian, J. V., *Cates' Primary Anatomy*, 4th ed. Baltimore: Williams & Wilkins Co., 1960.

Grant, J. C. Boileau, *A Method of Anatomy*, 6th ed. Baltimore: Williams & Wilkins Co., 1958.

———, *An Atlas of Anatomy*, 5th ed. Baltimore: Williams & Wilkins Co., 1962.

Gray, Henry, *Anatomy of the Human Body,* ed. Charles M. Goss, 27th ed. Philadelphia: Lea & Febiger, 1959.

Logan, Gene A., "Instructional Slides for Athletic Training and Rehabilitation." Springfield, Mo.: Box 3535 Glenstone Station.

———, et al., *Student Handbook for Adapted Physical Education.* Dubuque, Iowa: Wm. C. Brown Co., 1960.

Moseley, H. F., "Disorders of the Shoulder," *Ciba Clinical Symposia,* XI, No. 3 (1959), 75–102.

7

FORCES THAT AFFECT
MAN'S MOVEMENTS

Man's environment contains many forces and stresses that play upon his physical structure and sometimes bring about abnormal physical deviations. For the most part, deviations are due to the pull of gravity, congenital or pathological conditions, and traumatic musculoskeletal conditions. Conditions of a psychological nature may indirectly affect the physical structure in terms of psychosomatic or mind-body involvements. It is the purpose here to explain the role of exercise in helping the organism to counteract or adjust to the adaptations which result when one or more stresses or forces result in physical changes within the organism.

A concern for the prevention of adaptive changes in the elementary school child should be of primary importance. There should be a special emphasis on the prevention and amelioration of those adaptations which come about as a result of insufficient ability to counteract the force of gravity. It is during the elementary school years that the bones assume the internal structure and the external shape that is determined by the direction of the external pressures placed upon them. If these pressures are not in the proper balance or alignment required for normal growth relationships, the bones will tend to become abnormally formed. They may adapt in such a way as to become permanently fixed. For example, downward pressures applied with greater intensity on one side of the body of a vertebra than on the other will impede the growth of that side. Vertebral growth activity will be greater where the pressure is less intense. Structural changes may result from these imbalanced pressures.

If imbalances or poor postural habits are allowed to persist, they may encourage adaptive shortening of the connective tissues that bind the body together. Once such shortening has occurred, correcting the fault becomes more difficult. Stretching will be required before strength and endurance activities can become effective for the resumption of good alignment.

Exercise or physical activity in various forms can serve to counteract the effect of gravity. It can provide the strength, endurance, flexibility, and skill necessary for the maintenance of upright postures. The individual can make better use of his body as an instrument to perform the many tasks required in his daily living if he maintains it by exercising regularly. A well-conditioned body is not only more effective in counteracting the stresses of the pull of gravity, but it is also in a better state to perform efficient movements. A comprehensive consideration of the effects of gravity on the organism and the implications for programming in adapted physical education is presented in Chapter 8.

Environmental stresses that affect man's movement capacity may involve one or more of the bodily systems. Modifications of one's ability to move effectively may come about through various systemic changes; a change in the function of one system might cause negative or undesirable adaptations in another. Many handicapping conditions are congenital or pathological in nature. Generally, such impairment results from certain developmental insufficiencies, infections, diseases, and other causative factors.

There are many ways in which the individual with congenital and pathological conditions may be served through adapted physical education. In some instances, the physician's recommendation may be that sports and games which offer low energy output for their successful participation will provide the desired level of physical activity. Other individuals, with permanent conditions such as amputations, may be recommended for participation in activities that serve the purpose of physical maintenance. Still other students may benefit from individually prescribed exercises or a general conditioning program. Chapter 9 contains a discussion of congenital and pathological conditions affecting man, and some implications for adapted physical education.

A large percentage of students in adapted physical education classes have some form of musculoskeletal disability or deviation that has resulted from *trauma*. Since trauma is defined as an injury which comes from some external force, such injuries have a wide variety of causes. In some cases, the traumatic force upon a body part comes from the person's shifting quickly from one position to another. For example, trauma may result from lifting an object too quickly. The force in this case could cause compression or elongation of body parts or segments. A compression injury might be dealt to an intervertebral disc. Elongation is involved in the tearing of certain structures such as muscles, tendons, ligaments, and other forms of connective tissue. Musculoskeletal injuries usually include sprains, strains, dislocations and fractures. A discussion of injuries common to the musculoskeletal system is presented in Chapter 10.

8

GRAVITY AND POSTURAL ADAPTATIONS

THE SEARCH FOR EXTENSION

The human body wages a constant battle against the force of gravity. Even while we are asleep, we change positions numerous times to avoid discomfort. This discomfort is largely caused by pressure on the soft tissues between the bony structures and the supporting surface upon which the body is resting. Although it is possible to place the body in such a position as to negate the force of gravity momentarily, for all practical purposes, we are never free from this force.

Man, in assuming the upright, biped position, counteracts the force of gravity. Throughout his waking hours, much of his energy is expended solely in the maintenance of his antigravity, dynamic postures. In man's development process, certain neurological mechanisms—postural or spinal reflexes, for example—have become important in helping to sustain the body in antigravity relationships. These reflexes, which operate at a subcortical, involuntary level, provide man with the ability to maintain his antigravity positions without requiring his conscious attention. Other complex neurological mechanisms that operate to help man in his orientation to his spatial environment were discussed in Chapter 5.

Many problems arise in the maintenance of the upright, biped position. Not only must the muscles function to hold the body upright, but they must also serve to perform desired movements. Therefore, a complex interrelationship exists between antigravity functions and movement patterns requiring a great deal of skill. Generally, the extensors of the body perform the antigravity function and the flexors are responsible for the execution of skilled acts. These functions are not independent of each other. However, they may be more closely studied in terms of this dichotomy.

Antigravity Muscles

If the antigravity muscles do not have sufficient strength and endurance, certain negative adaptations may occur. For example, if the body is allowed to submit to the force of gravity, the connective tissues of the muscles antagonistic to the extensor muscles will tend to shorten adaptively. This may produce a decrease in range of motion or flexibility. Normal functioning will be inhibited, which may in turn encourage additional undesirable adaptations. Exercise plays a significant role in breaking this cycle, for the reversal of undesirable adaptations as well as from preventive and rehabilitative standpoints.

The muscles which compose the antigravity mechanism are illustrated in Figure 8.1. Certain joints of the body tend to succumb to the pull of gravity. These points, from an anterior-posterior view, are the ankle, knee, hip, and back. A minimum number of muscles must function at these joints to prevent "buckling." These muscles are: at the ankle, the gastrocnemius and soleus (A); at the knee, the quadriceps (B); and at the hip, the gluteus maximus (C). Included also in this series of antigravity muscles is the erector spinae group (D). The erector spinae acts to prevent the trunk from falling forward. It is attached along the spinal column between the sacrum and the base of the skull. The abdominal muscles (E) also serve a reflex antigravity function in holding the pelvis and the rib cage together when the erector spinae group acts to extend the spinal column. The abdominal muscles and erector spinae muscles work

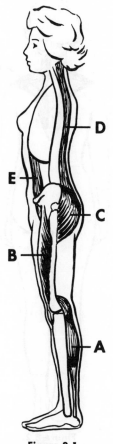

Figure 8.1

antagonistically in a paired relationship to help balance the body segments one over another.

Viewing the body from a posterior view, Figure 8.2, the remaining minimally essential group of muscles involved in the antigravity function are the scapular adductors (A). These consist mainly of the middle trapezius and the rhomboid-major and -minor

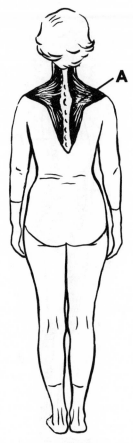

Figure 8.2

muscles. Their function is to hold the scapulae in their normal relationship, which in turn maintains the shoulders in balanced alignment upon the rib cage. Weakness of the scapular adductors allows
the shoulders to droop forward. This establishes a predisposition
that often results in adaptive shortening of the pectoral muscles of
the chest.

Effect of Gravity upon the Biped Position

The downward pull of gravity is a force that is capable of causing adaptations of various parts of the body when the biped position is assumed. These adaptations initially affect the skeletal system, because they alter the alignment of the bony levers at various joint articulations. Any adaptation affecting the skeletal system would consequently cause changes within the muscular system as well. Such changes involve the impairment of the muscular balance of those muscles that span the affected joints. This alteration occurs through the lengthening or stretching of one set of muscles and the shortening of its antagonists.

Posture is the result of man's adaptation to the force of gravity upon his biped position. The physical educator, therefore, must evaluate man's posture in order to determine the effectiveness of the individual's ability to resist the force of gravity. Effective adaptation may be characterized as facilitating normal physical growth and development in addition to permitting the individual to function most efficiently.

Unfortunately, when one speaks of posture, the connotation is usually that of an assumed, static, erect standing position. It is more appropriate and accurate to accept the concept of *postures,* because it provides the basis for a more functional approach to posture. Accordingly, effective and efficient function should be the key to "good postures." Development of strength and endurance in the muscles and flexibility in the joints is prerequisite for improved functioning. This development is essential if one is to assume and utilize efficient postures.

Although there appears to be a trend toward acceptance of the functional approach to postures, considerable emphasis is still being placed upon the aesthetic value that society places upon "good posture." Therefore, considerable time and energy is expended by teachers and students in an attempt to stimulate a standing posture which is identified as possessing "good" postural alignment.

The emphasis upon "good" standing posture has led to the practice of applying a single, rigid standard for body alignment to all people of all ages. Unfortunately, current practice is not always consistent with present knowledge. Concerning the practice of posture evaluation, the weight of authoritative opinion is against the use of a single standard applied to everyone. Morrison and Chenoweth stated their opposition to this practice when they wrote, "There is no definite form, shape, or standard for any part of the human body or for the body as a whole. It is impossible, therefore, to have a definite standard as regards posture."[1] Daniels, commenting on current practices of posture evaluation, voiced his opposition when he stated, ". . . that single rigid body mechanics specifications for all, regardless of body type and other factors which influence the human form, are scientifically unsupportable."[2] Goff, in an attempt to provide a standard that would take into consideration one's body type, developed orthograms of the anterior-posterior standing position for young adult white males. The orthograms for four types of body build were the result of the mean tracings of subjects in each group. This study purports to establish the criteria for normal posture on a scientifically sound basis.[3] Nonetheless, authoritative opinion agrees that "good" posture is largely an individual matter. Metheny has clearly stated this position:

> There is no one single best posture for all individuals. Each person must take the body he has and make the best of it. For each person the best posture is that in which the body segments are balanced in the position of least strain and maximum support. This is an individual matter.[4]

If one is not to make posture judgments based upon static standing, and if one must reject the use of a single standard which is applicable to all and evaluate posture on an individual basis, what criteria are to be used? This is the dilemma facing the physical educator today.

The primary justification for using the stationary standing position as the basis for postural evaluation is the aesthetic value

1 Whitelaw Reid Morrison and Laurence B. Chenoweth, *Normal and Elementary Physical Diagnosis,* 5th ed. (Philadelphia: Lea & Febiger, 1955), p. 86.

2 Arthur S. Daniels, *Adapted Physical Education* (New York: Harper & Row, Publishers, 1954), p. 310.

3 Charles Weer Goff, "Orthograms of Posture," *The Journal of Bone and Joint Surgery,* XXXIV-A (January 1952), 115–122.

4 Eleanor Metheny, *Body Dynamics* (New York: McGraw-Hill Book Co., Inc., 1952), p. 193.

placed on "good" posture by our society. The aesthetic appeal of erect posture, poise, and balance are not to be denied. Consequently, aesthetic and culturally determined standards cannot be ignored. Davis and Logan, in describing the aesthetic value of "good" posture stated:

> As is generally known, the individual who approaches, in appearance, the ideal posture which is established by the culture tends to present himself in a more favorable light. The ideal posture is taken as an indicator of a person's alertness and outlook on life in general. The aesthetic value of good posture should not be underestimated and the striving for this ideal is an asset to the individual.[5]

What, if any, are the characteristics of satisfactory criteria which may be used to evaluate postures? Morrison and Chenoweth advocated three conditions that must be met before any posture is classified as "good": "(1) does it make for mechanical freedom; (2) is it true to anatomical fact; (3) does it establish better functioning to one or more organs?"[6] Additional criteria may be drawn from the principles of *stability* and *balance* or *equilibrium*. The major principles that have been advanced concerning standing posture and which might serve as a basis for evaluation may be stated as (1) a body is in equilibrium when its center of gravity falls within its base and (2) the most stable position of a vertical segmented body is one in which the center of gravity of each weight-bearing segment lies in a vertical line directly over the base of support, or in which a deviation in one direction is exactly balanced in the opposite direction.

The application of the principles of stability to a standing position that is balanced and free from muscular and ligamentous strain would be that the line of gravity of the center of the head, chest, abdomen (trunk), and pelvis fall in a straight line. Furthermore, any displacement of a body segment would disturb the equilibrium of the whole body. Adjustments of other body segments would have to be made to regain and maintain equilibrium. The acceptance of the line of gravity as a guide to balanced posture has resulted in acceptance of the line of gravity as the criterion for ideal

---

[5] Elwood Craig Davis and Gene A. Logan, *Biophysical Values of Muscular Activity* (Dubuque, Iowa: Wm. C. Brown Co., 1961), p. 55.
[6] Morrison and Chenoweth, *Physical Diagnosis,* p. 86.

posture. Unfortunately, the early works of Christian Wilhelm Braune and Otto Fischer, published in 1889, concerning the determination of the center of gravity of the various body segments has been misinterpreted. It is now assumed by many physical educators that Braune and Fischer's findings represent a guide for the ideal posture. An interesting account of their work, in which four frozen cadavers were nailed to the wall in an attempt to determine the center and the line of gravity, is presented in an article by Hirt, Fries, and Hellebrandt.[7]

In the following discussion of screening for postural adaptations, specific check points are used for vertical and horizontal alignment. However, it must be clearly understood that these check points are to serve as general guides and are not presented as being absolute checks for "good" standing posture. When screening for adaptations or divergencies, *the physical educator should be more concerned with marked deviations than with slight or minor malalignments.*

The postural adaptations that man makes to the force of gravity may be grouped into two major classifications which serve as useful conceptual models. First, a *functional* divergency is one that involves only the soft tissues such as muscles or ligaments. A further qualification is that the divergency will disappear when the effect of gravity is eliminated. This tendency may be tested by (1) hanging or being suspended by the hands, (2) lying in a prone or supine position, or (3) assuming a bent-forward position. Second, a *structural* divergency is one in which bony change has occurred. It is a permanent condition. It does not disappear when the effect of gravity is removed.

It is important that functional adaptations be identified. The *appropriate* remedial action should be started as soon as possible. Immediate attention is required since marked postural adaptations place unusual and atypical stresses on the soft tissues, muscles, and ligaments of the body segment. Consequently, a marked joint or segmental malalignment places unusual stretch on some of the muscles and ligaments and causes a shortening of the opposing muscles and ligaments. The stretched muscles become weakened. The shortened muscles are stronger or more resistant to stretch, possibly as a result of adaptive shortening of the connective tissue. Such mus-

---

[7] Susanne E. Hirt, Corrine Fries, and F. A. Hellebrandt, "Center of Gravity of the Human Body," *Archives of Physical Therapy*, XXIX (1944), 280–287.

cular imbalance causes unusual muscular tension to be exerted on the bones. This force may be of sufficient intensity and duration to bring about changes in the external shape and internal structure of the bone in accordance with Wolff's law.

Improper functioning can and frequently does have a similar effect. Continuous coordinated muscular functioning which takes a body segment through its full range of motion is essential for efficient functioning of the body. If movements requiring limited range of motion are used habitually, some of the muscles of a joint cease to be used, or begin to function weakly. The corresponding muscles on the opposite side (antagonists), being relatively unopposed, begin to shorten and to decrease in extensibility. As a result, a muscular imbalance is established.

Although considerable material in this chapter is concerned with screening for postural adaptations on the basis of standing positions, it should be remembered that such assumed static positions are held only momentarily, if at all, in normal daily living. It is more logical to believe that all movement begins and ends with a posture. Hopefully, in-the-not-too-distant future, it will be possible effectively and efficiently to evaluate or screen the functional postures of man in his many activities of daily living.

It is imperative during the screening process that unilateral development and deviations be carefully noted and checked for relationship to total body structure or positioning. As a result of screening, those subjects with marked deviations who evidence pain or who have a limited range of motion should be immediately referred to a physician. An additional criterion for referral to a physician is the age of the subject. The very young child has pliable bones. This factor can make the condition more severe. But age can also be made to work for the correction of the condition. Therefore, remedial procedures should be undertaken as soon as possible. Remember, the means of correcting severe postural deviations must be based upon medical diagnosis and recommendations.

THE FEET

The feet function as the base of support for the body in a standing position. They also function as locomotor organs for propelling the body in movement.

The foot consists of seven tarsals, five metatarsals, and fourteen phalanges whose conformation presents a half-dome appearance. The foot is characterized by a longitudinal arch that runs anteroposteriorly from the base of the calcaneus to the heads of the five metatarsals. In reality, the longitudinal arch is five arches in one, the highest of which is on the medial aspect of the foot and terminates at the distal head of the first metatarsal. The arches terminating at the second, third, and fourth metatarsals become progressively lower until the arch of the fifth metatarsal is almost nonexistent. In addition, the longitudinal arch gives the impression of a transverse arch extending from the heads of the metatarsals to their proximal ends. This secondary arch, which exists noticeably across the more proximal ends of the metatarsals, is referred to as the *transverse* or *metatarsal* arch.

In the standing position, the weight of the body is transferred from the tibia directly to the talus, which in turn transfers half the weight downward to the calcaneus. The other half is transferred to the navicular, the "keystone" of the longitudinal arch. Through the navicular, the weight is distributed to the cuboid, the three cuneiforms, and through them to the metatarsals. Then, according to Grant, the weight is distributed equally to the heads of the second, third, fourth, and fifth metatarsals, and to each of the two sesamoid bones under the head of the first metatarsal.[8]

In the standing position, the line of gravity intersects the navicular and cuboid bones. The weight will be borne over these bones. Since the medial aspect of the longitudinal arch is much higher than that of the lateral arch, it is not as well adapted for weight bearing. But it provides the "give" or "spring" in the foot that prevents a "jar" in walking, running, or jumping.

Relationship of Foot Position to Weight Bearing

The feet in the upright body position are constantly being subjected to the force of gravity imposed by the body weight. Proper weight bearing is essential to the normal growth and development of the feet. Conversely, improper weight bearing can cause

---

[8] J. C. Boileau Grant, *A Method of Anatomy*, 6th ed. (Baltimore: Williams & Wilkins Co., 1958), pp. 456, 500.

structural divergencies of the feet. Abramson and Delagi have stated that weight bearing does bring about changes in the formation of bone. This idea corresponds to Wolff's law. Thus, as one adapts a weight-bearing position that varies the normal structural alignment of the foot, the muscles in the affected area are subjected to abnormal stress. Abramson and Delagi believe that the added muscular stress is of greater importance in the alteration of bony growth than is weight bearing *per se*. They conclude their discussion by stating, ". . . weight bearing does not develop sufficient degree and variety of stress while muscle action of sufficient magnitude is apparently capable of producing enough of both."[9] It is imperative that any evaluation of one's posture take into account the primary function of the feet, weight bearing.

Various anatomical movements and positions of the feet and ankles were discussed in Chapter 5. Attention is specifically called to the movements that occur at the transverse tarsal joint, *eversion* and *inversion,* since these are the movements or assumed positions of the foot in terms of the sole of the foot. The movements of the sole outward (eversion) and inward (inversion) are volitional. As such, they are easily observed.

One must also consider the movements and positions of *abduction* and *adduction* when discussing the feet. Much confusion arises in the use of these terms when discussing foot positions. Abduction and adduction are defined as the movement of a whole or part of a body segment toward (adduction) or away from (abduction) the midline of the body. Therefore, one must indicate whether the terms refer to the total foot or its distal aspect, the forefoot. Abduction and adduction of the whole foot are concomitants of rotation of the leg at the knee when the knee is flexed. These movements are performed by the whole limb if the knee is extended. However, these movements in the forefoot—with the action occurring at the metatarsal-phalangeal articulations—are so limited as to be almost nonexistent as volitional movements. The confusion is compounded when one considers abduction and adduction in terms of foot position.

9 Arthur S. Abramson and Edward F. Delagi, "The Contributions of Physical Activity to Rehabilitation," *Research Quarterly,* XXXI, No. 2, Pt. 2 (May 1960), 370.

Several authors discussing foot positions have introduced the terms "toeing-out" and "toeing-in." Unfortunately, they leave it to the reader to determine whether such terms refer to the position of the entire foot or to that of the forefoot.

In order to counteract such misunderstandings, functional definitions are given here for the terms *eversion, inversion, abduction,* and *adduction* to indicate anatomical movements or positions of the *total* foot. In reference to foot positions related to weight bearing in the standing position, the term *pronation* will indicate a position in which the foot is everted and the forefoot is abducted. *Supination* will indicate a position in which the foot is inverted and the forefoot is adducted. Foot positions are closely related to rotation of the thighs when the knees are extended. Therefore, when the thigh is rotated inward and the foot is free to move, the whole foot is adducted. If the foot is not free to move, as in the weight-bearing position, the torsion is then referred to the foot and ankle. The resultant force brings about pronation. Under similar conditions, but as a result of outward rotation, the positions of abduction and supination of the whole foot are achieved.

In terms of weight bearing, any foot position that shifts the weight to the medial border of the longitudinal arch will also abduct the forefoot. This movement is caused by the upper portion of the calcaneus rolling downward and inward. Thus, the relationship of the talus to the other tarsal bones changes. The tarsal-metatarsal and the metatarsal-phalangeal articulations have also had to make an adaptation, which results in a slight turning outward of the forefoot.

A weight-bearing position such as that just described, and which is characterized by those functional adaptations, is referred to as *pronation. Supination* is a foot position that shifts the weight to the outer border of the foot, and one in which, as a result of junctional adaptations of the bony structures of the foot, the forefoot is adducted.

The importance of proper foot position in relation to weight bearing cannot be overemphasized. The effect of gravity acting through the body weight is probably the direct cause of most foot problems. Therefore, any screening of the feet must include a determination of the subject's weight-bearing characteristics.

Screening Devices for Weight Bearing

Two devices are frequently used by physical educators for determining foot divergencies. The "pedograph," a foot-impression device, provides an inked foot impression. Although these impressions are commonly used, they are of little value since they place undue emphasis upon the height of the arch as an indicator of strength of the foot. There is little or no direct relationship between the height of the arch and foot strength. Two of the operational difficulties concerning the use of the inked foot impression are (1) that it is difficult to determine correctly the amount of ink to be used in order to achieve the best impression and (2) the impression is actually a composite of nonweight bearing and weight bearing because of the way the subject must step up on the equipment.

The second device is the "podiascope." This is of great value in determining the weight-bearing areas of the foot. The "podiascope," Figure 8.3, consists of a three-sided box, approximately 18 × 16 × 12 inches. The front of the box is open, and a mirror is inserted into the box. The mirror should be adjustable. The best angle is 45 degrees to the bottom of the box. The top of the box is of plate glass, not less than ½ inch in thickness. The subject stands on the glass top. The examiner looks into the mirror. The reflection of the feet in the mirror indicates the weight-bearing areas: the nonweight-bearing areas appear pink and the weight-bearing areas appear white. An additional advantage of the "podiascope" is that the examiner can accurately determine the effects of any weight-bearing changes that the subject makes at his suggestion.

Foot-Leg Alignment

There is a wide range of opinion about correct foot position. But from a functional approach, it is recommended that the foot position be one in which the feet are parallel, from 2 to 4 inches apart. This foot position is the natural or anatomic position; therefore, any suggestion of slight supination, in order to place the weight over the lateral border of the foot, is superfluous.

There is agreement concerning correct foot-leg alignment. Such alignment implies that certain bony landmarks will fall in a

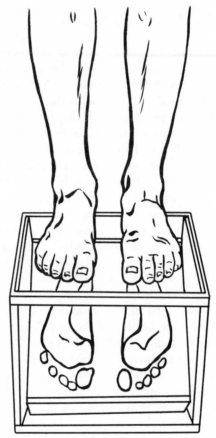

Figure 8.3

vertical line. The check points for such alignment when viewed from the front are the anterior inferior iliac spine, center of the patella, midpoint of the ankle, and the second toe. When viewed from the rear, a straight line should run through the midpoint of the popliteal space, the midline of the Achilles tendon, the midpoint of the ankle (note equal prominence of the malleoli), and the midline of the calcaneus.

Foot-leg alignment may be checked by use of a plumb line or by the use of a posture grid screen. Any marked deviation from the previously described vertical alignments should be noted carefully for further evaluation and possible referral to a physician.

Adaptations Resulting from Faulty Weight Bearing

Normal weight bearing is characterized by equal distribution between the heel and the ball of the foot (heads of the metatarsals). The weight which is referred to the ball of the foot is equally distributed. Because of the difference in the height of the medial and lateral borders of the longitudinal arch, the lateral or outer border of the foot is designed to absorb the imposed weight. Therefore, it is not unusual for a foot impression to show some degree of contact with the supporting surfaces as a result of the "giving" of the longitudinal arch in weight bearing. If the weight-bearing distribution is not normal as indicated by the "podiascope," it indicates that certain adaptations have occurred.

If there is weight bearing on the inner border of the foot with little or none on the lateral border or fifth metatarsal, the individual has assumed a position of pronation. Since the medial aspect of the arch is structurally weak and relatively unstable, it must rely on ligaments and muscles to maintain its integrity. Continuous weight bearing with the foot in a pronated position tends to cause the arch to become lower or flattened. Grant, in discussing the failure of the arch to maintain its correct position, stated:

. . . that failure of the arch is related to the duration of the stress to which it is subjected rather than to the severity of the stress . . . those who stand immobile subject their arches to relative continuous stress, and it is these latter who develop arch trouble.[10]

Therefore, although pronation may result in the lowering or flattening of the arch, it must not be assumed that a pronated foot is also a flat foot.

The determination of whether or not an individual's arch has fallen, and whether he has a flat foot, may be indicated by the use of either the "podiascope" (the inked foot impression may be used,

[10] Grant, *Method of Anatomy*, p. 495.

provided consideration is made of its limitations) or a functional arch-height test.

The functional arch-height test consists of the examiner sliding his extended second and third fingers (with the hand supinated) under the medial aspect of the longitudinal arch (the area of the first cuneiform and first metatarsal bones). The subject should be in his habitual standing position. If the examiner cannot slide his fingers under the arch or if the arch is resting on the supporting surface, the foot is classified as a flat foot, or *pes planus*. If the fingers can be slid only under the first metatarsal, the foot may be classified as having an unusually low arch. If the fingers can be slid under the proximal end of the second metatarsal, the foot may be classified as having a normal arch. If the fingers can be slid under the third or the fourth metatarsals, the foot is classified as having an unusually high arch. If the fingers can be slid under the fifth metatarsal or completely under the lateral border, the foot is classified as having an extremely high arch. If the arch is flexible, the condition is called a flexible high arch, or *pes cavus*. Once again, though, attention is called to the fact that authorities agree that there is little or no direct relationship between the height of the arch and the strength of the foot.

This discussion concerning the identification of foot adaptations resulting from improper weight bearing has dealt exclusively with observation based on the use of a "pedograph" or a "podiascope" and the functional arch-height test. However, there are also other signs and procedures that may be used to determine the presence of such adaptations.

By the utilization of a plumb line, it is possible to check the normal vertical foot-leg alignment previously described. If the individual has assumed undesirable foot positioning in his habitual standing posture, certain signs will become apparent (Fig. 8.4). In checking foot-leg alignment from the front, one should be aware of any noticeable changes in the conformation of the feet. The normal foot is slightly concave on the medial side due to the increased height of the medial aspect of the arch. The lateral border is slightly convex due to the lowness of the lateral aspect of the arch and the widening of the foot as a result of weight bearing. Therefore, the disappearance of concavity or the appearance of a slight convexity on the medial border is significant. These signs are indicative of the individual having assumed a position of pronation, with the weight being borne on the medial aspect of the foot (A, Fig. 8.4). Such a change in the conformation of the foot may also indicate that the individual has a low arch or a flat foot. However, additional screening with the use of a "podiascope" or the functional arch-height test should be made before classifying the foot as flat. Attention should also be focused on the position of the feet in relation to the normal parallel foot position.

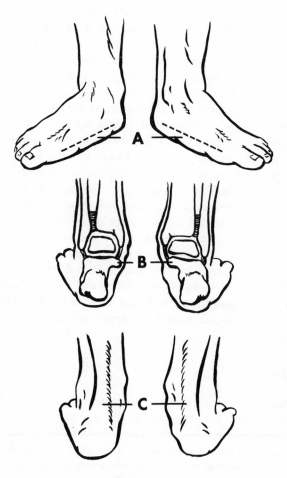

Figure 8.4

If the foot is in an abducted position, the whole foot pointing diagonally outward, the weight of the body is transferred to the medial border of the foot. This transfer places undue strain on the arch. If the whole foot is adducted, the weight is transferred to the inner border of the foot. Due to the rolling of the calcaneus as a result of improper weight bearing, there is a difference in the prominence of the malleoli. In a position of pronation, the upper aspect of the calcaneus rolls inward and downward. This results in the appearance of a "jamming" of the heel toward the fibular or lateral malleolus in which the lateral "ankle bone" seems to disappear (B, Fig. 8.4). The tibial malleolus appears to be further from the heel; consequently, it is more prominent. The reverse appearance is true in supination of the foot.

In checking foot-leg alignment from the rear, attention is called to the Achilles tendon and the malleoli. In typical or normal alignment, the Achilles tendon should be straight from its distal attachment on the calcaneus to the broadening of the gastrocnemius and soleus muscles. A noticeable bowing inward (C, Fig. 8.4), a convexity toward the medial aspect of the leg, is indicative of an adaptation in which the calcaneus has rolled inward and downward. This rolling increases the distance which the tendon must span and results in an increased tenseness of the tendon. Bowing inward is called *Achilles flare* or *Helbing's sign*. The appearance of an outward bowing is an indication of an assumed supinated position of the foot. Particular care must be taken to avoid the identification of the natural flaring of the calf muscles at their tendinous attachment as indicative of a flaring of the tendon itself. It is also possible from a rear view to notice undue prominence of the malleoli. Such a difference should be interpreted as previously discussed.

Weak Feet

There is a considerable difference of opinion about the classification and the relationship of the various faulty weight-bearing positions of the feet. The divergencies about which the controversy centers are pronation, flat feet, and weak feet. The definition and interrelationship of pronation and flat feet have been presented previously. The concept of weak feet has been purposely delayed, however, because of the controversy concerning the classification and definition of this divergency.

Weak feet have been treated by some authorities as synonymous with the position of abduction (pronation), in which the arch may or may not be depressed. They regard a pronated foot as a weak foot. Flat feet are also classified as weak feet. However, these same authorities indicate that the presence of pain should serve as the indicator of weak feet. Stafford and Kelly state, "The demarcation between normal and weak feet is not clear, except perhaps in the absence or presence of pain."[11] Morrison and Chenoweth have developed a functional test. In describing its use, they stated, "The following exercises are recommended. If they cause pain, weak feet may be suspected."[12] Consequently, if the testing movements produce pain, the foot should be classified as a weak foot.

Physical educators are primarily concerned with efficient and effective movement. It appears justified to use the functional foot test as a technique for determining whether or not a foot is to be classified as a weak foot. The functional test consists of four exercises. If during or immediately after the performance of any of the exercises the subject feels pain, he should be classified as having weak feet. Since the test is designed to place increasing stresses upon the feet, as soon as the subject feels pain he should stop rather than attempt to complete all of the test items or exercises. The exercises are described as follows (when the test or exercise includes the phrase "on toes," it means on the balls of the feet and toes; the phrase "feet abducted" implies the whole foot is pointing diagonally outward). (1) Rise on toes (feet abducted). (2) Walk on toes (with soles nearly vertical to the floor). (3) Hop on toes. (4) Jump into the air and land on the toes with feet abducted (knees relaxed).[13]

Other Foot Divergencies

Improper weight bearing and improperly fitted shoes may both cause bony malalignments in the anterior portion of the feet.

[11] George T. Stafford and Ellen Davis Kelly, *Preventive and Corrective Physical Education*, 3rd ed. (New York: Ronald Press Co., 1958), p. 200.
[12] Morrison and Chenoweth, *Physical Diagnosis*, p. 123.
[13] *Ibid.*

Malalignment frequently produces pain in the the plantar surface of the forefoot. This condition is *metatarsalgia*. It results from pressure exerted on the nerves in the metatarsal-phalangeal area. The pressure causes an inflammation or irritation of the nerves (neuritis). A frequent site of pain is the articulation of the fourth metatarsal with the first phalanx of the fourth toe. This pain is referred to as *true metatarsalgia* or as *Morton's metatarsalgia*—Dudley J. Morton was the first to describe it.

In normal weight bearing, the weight is borne anteriorly on the heads of the metatarsals except for the first metatarsal where the weight is taken by the two sesamoid bones. Therefore, if there is displacement of any of the metatarsal-phalangeal articulations for any cause, the toe is unable to maintain its normal position of extension. As a consequence, the first phalanx is hyperextended, the second phalanx is flexed, and the third or distal phalanx may be either flexed or extended. As a result, the toe assumes the appearance of a hammer. This divergency is called *hammer toe*. In addition to the hammer shape, one will note on closer examination of the dorsal surface of the foot that the extensor tendon of the first phalanx is very prominent. This prominence is due, in part, to the hyperextended position of the phalanx. Further examination of the plantar surface of the foot will frequently reveal a *callus* under the head of the metatarsal of the affected toe.

Ill-fitting shoes create friction or pressure. The body in defense to this additional force develops a thickening of the skin, or callus. When located on top of or between the toes, this protective thickening of the skin is referred to as a *corn*. Pressure or friction continuously applied by ill-fitting shoes causes crowding or squeezing of the toes. Frequently, the fourth and fifth toes overlap. The fifth toe is usually forced under the fourth toe. This divergency is called *overlapping toes*.

The great toe is also susceptible to increased pressure caused by improper shoes. The hallux, or great toe, is deflected or turned toward the four lesser toes. This divergency is called *hallux valgus*. An apparent concomitant of this condition is the development of a *bunion* and *exostosis* of the bone. With the great toe being deflected toward the other toes, the pressure of ill-fitting shoes is exerted against the side of the head of the first metatarsal. The articulation of the first metatarsal and the proximal phalanx of the great toe is

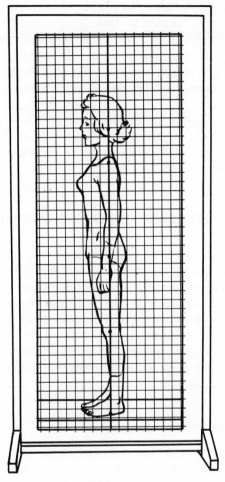

Figure 8.5

unique in that a *bursa* is present. The pressure results in irritation of the bursa, which becomes inflamed and is known as *bursitis*. Enlargement of the bursa is called a bunion. As a consequence of the enlargement, in addition to the original pressure, the body deposits calcium in the area of the head of the first metatarsal in response to the increased irritation. The deposit of additional calcium increases the size and alters the shape of the metatarsal. This action causes further friction. The outward growth of bone as described is referred to as exostosis. When this bony change has occurred, surgical intervention is the only effective method of treatment. It is imperative that hallux valgus be identified early so that corrective measures may be undertaken before the condition becomes structural.

Rasch and Burke, in their discussion of the importance of the feet to proper body alignment, concluded, "Structural or functional foot abnormalities must be corrected or compensated before good posture can be achieved."[14]

ANTERIOR-POSTERIOR ADAPTATIONS

The screening for anterior-posterior postural adaptations involves the use of a plumb line or a posture grid screen. The standing position viewed laterally should demonstrate vertical alignment (Fig. 8.5). When checking for marked deviations of vertical alignment, the following anatomical landmarks may serve as a guide: base of the fifth metatarsal (approximately 1 to $1\frac{1}{2}$ inches in front of lateral malleolus); behind the patella; midpoint of the conformation of the hip; midpoint of the conformation of the shoulder; and the lobe of the ear.

Foot-Leg Alignment

Vertical alignment was described earlier in terms of a vertical line between the second toe, the midpoint of the ankle, middle of the patella, and the anterior inferior iliac spine. However, when assessing anterior-posterior deviations, it is necessary to observe the body from the side. Therefore, new check points are needed as the basis for determining normal alignment.

The normal position of the foot is at a *right angle* to the leg. The line of gravity falls at the front edge of the tibia and in front of the malleolus in the area of the navicular-cuboid articulation.

---

[14] Philip J. Rasch and Roger K. Burke, *Kinesiology and Applied Anatomy*, 2nd ed. (Philadelphia: Lea & Febiger, 1963), p. 371.

Therefore, the check points for normal foot-leg alignment are just behind the patella for the knee, and from 1 to 1½ inches in front of the fibular malleolus. A plumb line provides the vertical reference line.

If there is a marked deviation from this line, it will indicate either an increase or a decrease of the foot-leg angle. If the check point of the knee—back edge of the patella—is noticeably forward of the reference line, the individual has assumed a position of partial dorsiflexion, or forward inclination of the leg at the ankle. If the check point is considerably behind the vertical, the individual has assumed a position of partial plantar flexion or backward inclination of the leg at the ankle joint.

Leg-Thigh Alignment

The tibia and the femur articulate at the knee joint. The normal position of both the knee and the hip is extension, but not complete extension. The femur and tibia should form a straight line. The line of gravity passes through the greater trochanter. The check point for vertical alignment of the thigh at the hip is the midpoint of the conformation of the hip. By use of a plumb line, the vertical alignment for the leg and thigh should fall behind the patella and through the midpoint of the hip.

Due to the relationship of foot-leg alignment to the position of the knees, any deviation of the foot-leg angle will affect leg-thigh alignment. A decrease in the foot-leg angle (dorsiflexion) will place the tibia anterior to the vertical. This will cause flexion of the thigh at the hip in order for the femur to articulate with the tibia. These actions result in partial flexion of the knees. An increase in the foot-leg angle (plantar flexion) causes the thigh to be hyperextended. The result is an assumed position of hyperextension of the knees. This position is referred to as "back knee" or *genu recurvatum.*

Pelvic Alignment

The pelvis has been identified as the "keystone" of standing posture (Fig. 8.6), because of its function of supporting the upper

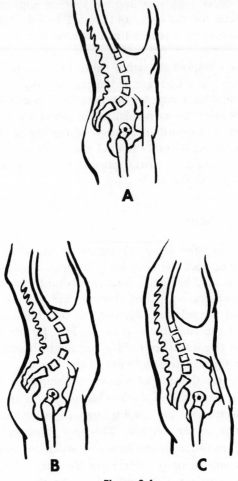

Figure 8.6

body weight and transferring it to the legs and feet. There is general agreement that the normal alignment of the pelvis consists of a slight forward and downward inclination. Normal pelvic alignment is present if the anterior superior iliac spine and the anterior aspect of the pubic crest, or symphysis pubis, are vertically aligned (A, Fig. 8.6). This pelvic alignment is commonly checked by use of a plumb line. If the anterior superior iliac spine (a.s.i.s.) is forward of the symphysis pubis, the pelvis has been rotated forward and downward. This position is called *increased pelvic inclination* (B, Fig. 8.6). Conversely, if the symphysis pubis is anterior to the a.s.i.s., the pelvis has been rotated backward. This position is called *decreased pelvic inclination* (C, Fig. 8.6).

An additional check for pelvic inclination involves the determination of the angle between the lumbo-sacral junction and the symphysis pubis. Pelvic inclination is considered normal when this angle is 50 to 60 degrees from the horizontal. However, it is extremely difficult to measure accurately pelvic inclination in the living subject.[15]

Thigh-Pelvic Relationship

The inclination of the pelvis is controlled by the hip flexors, the hip extensors, the extensors of the lumbar spine, and the abdominals. In the aligned, balanced position, there is equal muscle tension exerted on the pelvis by these muscle groups. If, however, there is greater muscular tension exerted by the hip flexors or the extensors of the lumbar spine, the inclination of the pelvis will be increased; whereas, if there is greater muscular tension exerted by the hip extensors and/or the abdominals, the inclination of the pelvis is decreased.

Since the rectus femoris and the hamstrings are two-joint muscles, affecting both the knee and the hip joints, any change in the tension or length of these muscles tends to change the position of the knee and hip joints. Flexion of the knees results in lengthening the rectus femoris. This creates greater tension, or a downward pull on the anterior aspect of the pelvis. This downward pull increases pelvic inclination. Hyperextension of the knees results in placing a stretch on the hamstrings, and this creates a downward pull on the posterior aspect of the pelvis, thereby decreasing pelvic inclination.

Pelvic-Lumbar Relationship

The sacrum, which occupies the medial-posterior portion of the pelvic girdle, is an immovable segment of the spine. The

---

[15] Rasch and Burke, *Kinesiology*, p. 372.

superior surface of the sacrum provides the base for articulation of the movable segments of the lumbar spine. Due to the fixed position of the sacrum, any movement of the pelvic girdle will have a direct relationship to the position of the lumbar segment of the spine (Fig. 8.6). It is impossible, therefore, to separate the curve of the lumbar spine from the inclination of the pelvis. Consequently, if the pelvic inclination is increased, the sacrum rotates forward and downward, causing the lower lumbar vertebrae also to assume a position of forward inclination. The body in an attempt to maintain a balanced upright position will compensate by assuming a posterior inclination of the upper portion of the lumbar spine and lower portion of the thoracic spine. This position results in an exaggeration in the lumbar curve (B, Fig. 8.6). If the pelvic inclination is decreased, the sacrum rotates backward and downward, causing the lower lumbar vertebrae also to assume this inclination. The compensating adaptations for this unnatural position result in a decrease in the normal lumbar curve (C, Fig. 8.6).

An additional concomitant associated with increased pelvic inclination is the anterior displacement or sagging of the abdominal viscera. The abdominal muscles, through their attachment to the pubis, influence the inclination of the pelvis. The abdominals are elongated and the pressure of the viscera adds further stress to the muscles when the pelvic inclination is increased. The protrusion or sagging of the abdominal viscera is known as *visceral ptosis* (B, Fig. 8.6). When the pelvic inclination is decreased and the pubis is rotated forward and upward, the lower portion of the abdominal area becomes prominent (C, Fig. 8.6). This prominence is most noticeable in the female because of the development of a layer of adipose tissue in the area between the pubis and umbilicus. However, it must be remembered that ptosis is an actual sagging of the abdominal viscera, and is not necessarily synonymous with a prominent abdomen.

Lumbar Spine

The normal lumbar spine is characterized by a moderate anterior hyperextension curve, when viewed laterally (A, Fig. 8.6). There is no absolute standard for the determination of the degree or extent of the anterior convexity of the normal lumbar curve.

When observing a student's standing posture, one must be alert for marked changes in the angulation of the lumbar curve. A marked increase in the lumbar curve is called a *hollow back* or *lumbar lordosis* (B, Fig. 8.6). Lordosis implies an increase or exaggeration of a forward or anterior curve. A marked decrease in the lumbar curve is called a flat back or *lumbar kyphosis* (C, Fig. 8.6). Kyphosis implies an increase or exaggeration of a backward or posterior curve, or, as in this instance, a decrease or reversal of a forward curve.

Thoracic Spine and Shoulder Girdle

The normal thoracic curve is characterized by a moderate posterior flexion curve when viewed laterally. A severe angulation or hump as well as a marked increase in the thoracic or dorsal curve is called "round upper back," *thoracic* or *dorsal kyphosis.* The check point for alignment of the shoulders in terms of upright standing is the midpoint of the conformation of the shoulder. The vertical alignment is from the midpoint of the hip to the midpoint of the shoulder. A plumb line may be used for determining vertical alignment.

Because of the use of the hands and arms in manipulation, it is obvious that such actions require the shoulder girdle to assume a position of protraction. Continuous use of this position results in a shortening of the anterior muscles, which would pull the shoulders forward and abduct the scapulae. Because of the forward position of the shoulders, the chest will appear sunken or shallow. If the forward position or protraction is maintained habitually and if the divergency is marked, the midpoint of the shoulder will be anterior or forward to the vertical reference line. This condition is called "round shoulders" or "forward shoulders."

An apparent increase in the thoracic curve may be due to the protraction of the shoulders and abduction of the scapulae. This frequently results in the faulty assumption that forward shoulders and round upper back are synonymous. Faulty identification of an upper thoracic divergency is further complicated, since forward shoulders frequently accompany thoracic kyphosis. Therefore, one must be especially careful and remember that different bony structures are involved. Thoracic kyphosis is a spinal divergency. Conversely, forward shoulders imply a divergency of the shoulder girdle. A simple and valuable check is to ask the subject to retract his shoulders, or adduct his scapulae. If he is able to do this and the check point of the shoulder regains vertical alignment, it may be assumed that the divergency is forward shoulders and not thoracic kyphosis.

Another concomitant of protraction of the shoulder girdle with the accompanying abduction of the scapulae is the protrusion of the vertebral border of the scapulae from the rib cage. This condition is influenced by the muscular imbalance between the scapular adductors and abductors. The protrusion of the scapulae is known as "winged scapulae."

Lumbar-Thoracic Relationship

Deviations or changes involving only one spinal segment have been discussed previously. Although an adaptation may occur exclusively in one spinal segment, a change in alignment generally involves more than one segment due to the process of compensation. The most common combined or compound thoracic-lumbar adaptation is one in which there is an increase in the normal curve of both the thoracic and the lumbar spines. This condition is referred to as a "round hollow back" or *kypholordosis*.

Another adaptation which involves both the thoracic and lumbar curves is one in which the thoracic curve tends to obliterate or reduce the lumbar curve. This deviation terminates in sharp hyperextension at the lumbo-sacral junction. This condition is referred to as a "round sway back." At first glance, the condition appears to be an increase in the thoracic curve. Because of the prominence of the buttocks, there appears to be an increase in the lumbar curve. Close examination will show that neither the lumbar or thoracic curve is increased. The thoracic curve is not increased, but it does extend through the thoracic as well as the lumbar segments of the spine. Consequently, the lumbar curve is decreased or reversed as characterized by a "flat back," or lumbar kyphosis. However, because of the resultant posterior overhang of the trunk, there is a sharp hyperextension at the lumbo-sacral junction. The prominence of the buttocks in many instances gives a shelf-like appearance. This frequently leads one to assume falsely that the lumbar curve has a sharply increased angulation.

Cervical Spine and Head Position

The normal cervical spine is characterized by a moderate anterior hyperextension curve when viewed laterally. A marked or exaggerated increase in the cervical curve is called "poke neck" or *cervical lordosis,* whereas a decrease in the cervical curve is called "flat neck" or *cervical kyphosis.*

The position of the head, partially due to its mass, has an effect on the musculature of the cervical spine. The balanced position of the head is one in which the vertical alignment passes through the midpoint of the conformation of the shoulder and the lobe of the ear. If the vertical reference check point of the head and lobe of the ear is significantly anterior to the line, and if the chin is down and back, the head position is referred to as "forward head." Conversely, if the lobe of the ear is posterior to the reference line, and the chin is forward and up, this position is referred to as "back head." Because of the mass of the head, the cervical spine adapts to various head positions. A "forward head" position is commonly associated with a somewhat decreased cervical curve. The "back head" position is usually associated with an increased cervical curve.

One may speculate about the validity of the commonly held standard for head positioning. The study of Braune and Fischer, previously cited, utilized frozen cadavers. It is assumed that the cadavers were frozen while in the anatomical supine position. If this assumption is correct, the head, because of its mass and relationship to the supporting surface, may have assumed an extreme posterior position. Ironically, this may account for the unusually high incidence of students who are assigned to adapted physical education because of a "forward head" divergency.

Thoracic-Cervical Relationship

Both the thoracic and cervical segments of the spine are characterized by moderate curves. Resultant changes involving only the thoracic or cervical curves have been discussed previously. Although adaptations may be confined to only one segment, any change in the thoracic curve is generally compensated by, or affects, the cervical segment of the spine. Recalling the discussion of the relationship of "round upper back" and "forward shoulders," it will become apparent that as the body attempts to compensate for the posterior thrust of the increased thoracic curve, the shoulders must be brought forward so that the weight of the arms may assist in maintaining a balanced position. A similar relationship exists between the position of the head and the adaptations of the thoracic area. In other words, the head is thrust partly forward as a compensatory reaction. In addition, the head is frequently held in a forward position as a result of "looking" while reading or performing manipulative skills. Consequently, "forward head" and a decreased cervical curve are generally associated with "round upper back" and "forward shoulders."

Compound Anterior-Posterior Adaptations

Previous discussion of anterior-posterior adaptations of one's standing position has been primarily concerned with segmental changes. Some indication of the interrelationship of the various body segments has been shown. However, no attempt has been made to demonstrate total body adaptations commonly assumed in standing (Fig. 8.7). The individual attempts to maintain a balanced posture in which the weight of the head is balanced over the center of the trunk. This weight, in turn, is centered over the pelvis. The weight is borne equally by the thighs and distributed to the legs and finally to the feet (A, Fig. 8.7). Thus, any marked change in normal alignment will be referred to or will affect other body segments.

Any analysis of the standing position should begin with the feet, because they provide the base of support. Any marked deviation at this level will necessitate adaptations in other body segments higher on the body.

There are two major classifications of commonly assumed—consciously or unconsciously—standing postural adaptations that will illustrate the concept of total body postural compensation. The first example is frequently referred to as the "fatigue slump posture"

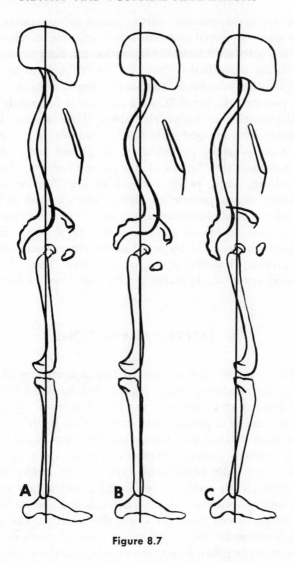

Figure 8.7

(B, Fig. 8.7). This position is characterized by the weight being borne on the medial-posterior aspect of the feet. There is an increase in the foot-leg angle, hyperextension of the knees, increased pelvic inclination, increased lumbar curve, sagging abdominal viscera, increased thoracic curve, protracted shoulders, apparent sunken chest, abducted and protruding scapulae, decreased cervical curve, and a forward head. This position has been described as one in which the individual is "hanging" or "riding" on his ligaments. The other position is commonly referred to as the "debutante slouch posture" (C, Fig. 8.7). This position is frequently associated with the wearing of high-heeled shoes. This position is assumed consciously by teen-aged girls and by women in an attempt to decrease the posterior projection of the gluteal area. The primary differences from the "fatigue slump posture" are in relation to the foot and leg, knee, pelvic inclination, and lumbar curve. The "debutante slouch posture" is characterized by the weight being borne on the medial-anterior aspect of the feet, decreased foot-leg angle, partial flexion of the knees, decreased pelvic inclination, prominent abdomen, decreased lumbar curve, increased thoracic curve, protracted shoulders, apparent sunken chest, abducted and protruding scapulae, decreased cervical curve, and a forward head.

LATERAL ADAPTATIONS

The determination of marked lateral deviations of body segments in the standing position requires the use of both the anterior and posterior views. Screening for lateral postural adaptations involves the use of a posture grid screen. This method is necessary because both vertical and horizontal alignment must be checked.

In normal vertical alignment, viewed from the rear, the reference line falls equidistant between the ankles and knees, passes through the cleft of the buttocks, and bisects the midline of the spinous processes of the vertebrae and the midline of the head. When viewed from the front, the reference line falls equidistant between the ankles and knees; passes through the midpoint of the symphysis pubis; bisects the umbilicus and the midline of the sternum, chin, and nose; and passes between the eyes.

In order to determine adequately whether there is lateral asymmetry of the body segments in the standing position, it is essential to check horizontal alignment. When viewed from the front, the following body structures should be in horizontal align-

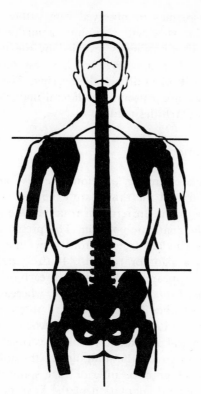

Figure 8.8

ment: the patellae, the anterior superior iliac spines, and the shoulders. When viewed from the rear, the scapulae and the shoulders should be horizontally aligned (Fig. 8.8).

Foot-Ankle Adaptations

The primary lateral deviations of the foot and ankle were discussed more fully in the section concerning the feet. But because of the relationship of faulty weight bearing or foot positioning to lateral deviations, a brief review of the foot is presented here. Pronation of the foot, in addition to weight bearing on the medial border of the foot, is characterized by a prominent medial or tibial malleolus. This sign may be observed from either a front or rear view. The posterior view will also show a medial bowing of the Achilles tendon. This bowing is revealed by the use of a vertical reference line. The feet may, however, have assumed a position of supination as a result of faulty weight bearing. The signs of such a position of the foot are a prominent lateral malleolus and an outward bowing of the Achilles tendon.

Leg-Thigh Alignment

In the normal standing position, the feet are parallel, the knees are extended, and the thighs are extended. There should be no rotation of the thighs. In terms of rotation, the normal position of the thighs is the anatomic position. The presence of rotation of the thighs can be checked from a front view: the position of the patellae serves as a sign for rotation. If the patellae are turned inward, giving the appearance of looking at each other "cross-eyed," they indicate *inward rotation* of the thighs, whereas, if the patellae are turned outward, they indicate *outward rotation* of the thighs.

The normal position of the knees, when viewed from the front, is one of vertical alignment. A simple vertical check in which the reference line intersects the midpoint of the ankle, the midline of the knee, and the anterior inferior iliac spine may be used. A further check for lateral adaptation of the knee position is one in which the subject stands with the feet together and parallel and with the patellae pointing straight ahead (A, Fig. 8.9). In this position, the medial malleoli and the medial aspect of the knees should be in contact. If the knees are not in vertical alignment, it is indicative that some adaptation has taken place in relation to knee position. Frequently, a common functional adaptation is mistakenly identified as "bowlegs" (B, Fig. 8.9). This apparent bowing of the legs and knees is due to the individual's assuming a position of hyperextension of the knees. This position is associated with inward rotation of the thighs as indicated by the apparent inward rotation of the patellae. This condition is appropriately called "functional bowlegs" since its characteristics readily disappear when the subject outwardly rotates the thighs while assuming the normal extended position of the knees. If the knees do not touch when standing with the feet together, the individual has "bowlegs," or *genu varum*

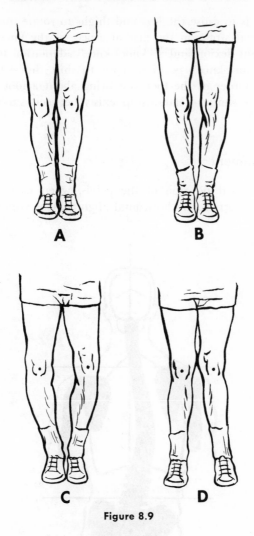

Figure 8.9

(C, Fig. 8.9). If the knees are in contact and the subject is unable to place the feet together and parallel so that the medial malleoli are in contact, the individual has "knock-knees," or *genu valgum* (D, Fig. 8.9).

Improper weight bearing or foot positioning is associated with lateral knee adaptations. Continuous weight bearing in a pronated position tends to cause the legs and thighs to rotate inward, which places unusual stress on the medial aspect of the knee and tends to cause slight flexion and a "knock-knee" adaptation to occur. An assumed "knock-knee" position tends to shift the weight toward the medial border of the foot and bring about a foot position of pronation. A similar relationship exists between supination and "bowlegs."

Pelvic Alignment

The normal position of the pelvis, when viewed from the front, is characterized by horizontal alignment or symmetry of the

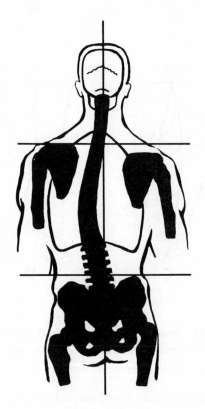

Figure 8.10

anterior superior iliac spines. This alignment may be checked by use of the horizontal lines on a grid screen. If these points are not aligned, it is indicative of a lateral tilt of the pelvis. This deviation may result from a difference in leg length that may be due to improper foot position, knee deviation, or a structural disorder. If the pelvic tilt is due to a difference in leg length, the curve of the waistline on the side of the longer leg is curved inward and is accompanied by a soft-tissue fold at the waistline. The hip of the longer leg is prominent and rotated slightly forward. These characteristics are due to a shifting of the trunk from the vertical line so that it is no longer equally balanced over the base of support. Displacement of a body segment can be checked by use of a plumb line (Figs. 8.10 and 8.11).

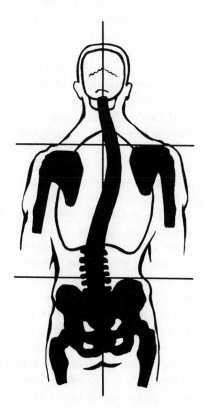

Figure 8.11

Lateral Spinal Adaptations

Postural adaptation of the spine in a lateral direction is called *scoliosis*. Scoliosis means bending, twisting, or rotating. Two of the characteristics of scoliosis are primarily concerned with vertebral adaptations. They are identified as deviation and rotation. The term "deviation" is used to indicate lateral movement of the vertebrae from the normal vertical alignment. The term "rotation" is used to indicate the turning or twisting of the spinous process of the vertebrae about the normal vertical alignment. An additional characteristic of scoliosis which is primarily concerned with the segments of the trunk is displacement. This term refers to the shifting of a trunk segment from the normal balanced position over the base of support, the feet. Deviation and displacement may be checked by use of a plumb line. Rotation may be checked by having the subject bend forward from the waist with the arms hanging down. This position is called the *Adams' position* (Fig. 8.12).

An additional characteristic of scoliosis involves muscular adaptation. If one continuously assumes a position in which the spine is laterally flexed to the right, the muscles on the right side will undergo adaptive shortening. The atrophied muscles on the left side will be elongated or stretched. In addition, muscular imbalance of the deeper muscles must be considered, since they may be a major factor in producing scoliosis. The resultant muscular imbalance limits the lateral flexibility of the spine.

Functional postural adaptations involve changes in muscular or ligamentous tissue, and the signs of the divergency will usually disappear when the effect of gravity is eliminated—either by hanging by the hands or assuming the Adams' position.

Structural adaptations involve bony change. The atypical characteristics do not disappear when gravity is eliminated. An additional characteristic that may be used to classify a lateral divergency as either functional or structural is the appearance of a bulge on either side of the spine while standing. This prominence may also be seen in the Adams' position. In a functional scoliosis, there is a muscular bulge in the area of the concavity of the curve that results from the adaptive shortening of the muscles. Although the lateral curve may disappear, this bulge is evident in the Adams'

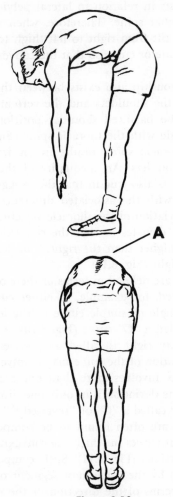

Figure 8.12

position. A bony bulge on the side of the convexity of the curve is characteristic of a structural scoliosis. This bulge is due to the protrusion of the ribs as a result of rotation by the thoracic vertebrae.

In the discussion of anterior-posterior postural adaptations, it was impossible to separate pelvic inclination and the lumbar curve because of the fixed position of the sacrum. The same type of relationship also exists in relation to lateral pelvic tilt and lateral deviation of the lumbar spine. Therefore, when viewed from the rear, a lateral pelvic tilt from right to left (high to low) causes the lumbar spine to deviate or curve so that the convexity is to the left (Fig. 8.10).

A similar relationship also exists between the balanced horizontal alignment of the shoulders and the vertebrae of the upper thoracic spine. In the balanced shoulder position, the shoulders form a 90-degree angle with the thoracic spine (Fig. 8.8). A lateral deviation of the thoracic spine results in an imbalance or displacement of the shoulders. An inequality of the axillary angles results. The converse is also true in that the exaggerated difference in shoulder heights with the associated difference of the axillary angles indicates a deviation of the thoracic vertebrae. For example, if the thoracic spine deviates so that the convexity is to the left, the left shoulder is higher than the right. The left axillary angle is smaller than the right (Fig. 8.10).

Scoliotic curves are defined in terms of their convexities. They are called or identified, for example, as either *convexity right* or *right convexity*. A single or simple curve to the left, or *convexity left*, is commonly called a "C" curve (Fig. 8.10). A lateral curve to the right or convexity right is called a "reversed C" curve. Although a lateral deviation of the spine may involve only one spinal segment, it frequently involves more than one segment. In either instance, as long as the deviation is in only one direction, the curve may be appropriately called a "C" or "reversed C" curve.

Scoliotic curves are often found to be compound. They can consist of two different curves in which the convexities of the curves are in opposite directions (Fig. 8.11). Such compound curves are defined two ways: (1) by the uppermost segment of the spine that deviates, and (2) in terms of the direction of the convexity of the curves. For example, a compound curve in which the thoracic curve is to the left and the lumbar curve is to the right is defined as a *thoracic left–lumbar right*. It can also be called an "S" curve. A compound curve in which the thoracic curve is to the right and the lumbar curve is to the left is defined as *thoracic right–lumbar left*. It can also be called a "reversed S" curve (Fig. 8.11).

Some of the characteristics or interrelationships of scoliosis may be generalized. If there is a lateral pelvic tilt, the convexity of the lumbar spine will be in the direction of the lower hip. If there is a lateral thoracic curve, the high shoulder will be on the side of the convexity. In simple or single curves the low hip and high shoulder are on the same side. If there is a compound curve, the low hip and shoulder are on the same side. One should differentiate between scoliotic curves by either defining them in terms of the convexity of the curves or describing them in terms of their characteristics of deviation, displacement, and rotation. So far, this discussion has been in terms of asymmetry of body segments—displacement—and a spinal deviation. Scoliosis possesses a third characteristic, rotation of the vertebrae.

Rotation of the vertebrae in scoliosis is most noticeable in the thoracic area when the ribs are affected by the rotation of the vertebrae. Thoracic rotation is indicated by the prominence of one side of the chest as seen from the front. A rear view will also show a prominence of one side of the rib cage when rotation is present. For example, in a "reversed C" curve of the thoracic area, the thorax is more prominent in the front on the left side. Posteriorly, the ribs are more prominent on the right side. A further check for vertebral rotation utilizes the forward-bend or Adams' position. In this position, a prominence of the thorax on the side of the convexity is noticeable if rotation is present.

The interrelations between the characteristics of deviation and rotation of the thoracic vertebrae in scoliosis is often a source of misunderstanding. The lateral adaptation is primarily one of lateral flexion. Part of the confusion arises from the fact that although the spine is laterally flexed the direction of a scoliotic curve is described in terms of its convexity. For example, if the thoracic spine is laterally flexed to the right, the resultant curve is described as a *dorsal* or a *thoracic left scoliosis*. In order to perform marked lateral flexion, the vertebrae must rotate. Thus, in order laterally to flex the thoracic spine to the right to its anatomical limit of flexibility, the thoracic vertebrae must rotate to the right. In terms of the direction of the vertical deviation or lateral curve, the vertebrae rotate toward the side of the concavity.

The physician, when prescribing unilateral exercises for the correction or amelioration of the scoliotic curve, will employ the "derotation principle"—the prescribed exercises will involve rotating the thoracic spine in the direction opposite to its assumed position. For example, in the case of a dorsal left scoliosis, derotation exercises will involve rotation of the vertebrae to the left. In terms of the characteristics of the curve, the rotation will be in the direction of the curve's convexity. The derotation exercises will also involve lateral flexion of the thoracic spine. The lateral flexion in the above case will be to the left, the direction of the convexity of the curve.

Those who are interested in pursuing research in the area of measurement and evaluation of posture and body mechanics are referred to Clarke and Clarke,[16] and Mathews, Kruse, and Shaw.[17]

Selected References

Abramson, Arthur S., and Edward F. Delagi, "The Contributions of Physical Activity to Rehabilitation," Research Quarterly, XXXI, No. 2, Pt. 2 (May 1960), 365–375.

Clarke, H. Harrison, and David H. Clarke, Developmental and Adapted Physical Education. Englewood Cliffs, N.J.: Prentice-Hall, Inc., 1963.

Corrective Physical Education: Teaching Guide for Junior and Senior High Schools. Los Angeles City Schools, Division of Instructional Services, Pub. No. SC-566.

Daniels, Arthur S., Adapted Physical Education. New York: Harper & Row, Publishers, 1954.

Davis, Elwood Craig, and Gene A. Logan, Biophysical Values of Muscular Activity. Dubuque, Iowa: Wm. C. Brown Co., 1961.

Drew, Lillian Curtis, and Hazel L. Kinzly, Individual Gymnastics, 5th ed. Philadelphia: Lea & Febiger, 1949.

Fait, Hollis F., Adapted Physical Education. Philadelphia: W. B. Saunders Co., 1960.

Goff, Charles Weer, "Orthograms of Posture," The Journal of Bone and Joint Surgery, XXXIV-A (January 1952), 115–122.

Grant, J. C. Boileau, A Method of Anatomy, 6th ed. Baltimore: Williams & Wilkins Co., 1958.

[16] H. Harrison Clarke and David H. Clarke, Developmental and Adapted Physical Education (Englewood Cliffs, N.J.: Prentice-Hall, Inc., 1963).
[17] Donald K. Mathews, Robert Kruse, and Virginia Shaw, The Science of Physical Education for Handicapped Children (New York: Harper & Row, Publishers, 1962).

Hirt, Susanne E., Corrine Fries, and F. A. Hellebrandt, "Center of Gravity of the Human Body," *Archives of Physical Therapy*, XXIX (1944), 280–287.

Howland, Ivalclare Sprow, *Adapted Physical Education in Schools.* Dubuque, Iowa: Wm. C. Brown Co., 1959.

Kelly, Ellen Davis, *Teaching Posture and Body Mechanics.* New York: A. S. Barnes & Co., 1949.

Kendall, Henry O., Florence P. Kendall, and Dorothy A. Boyton, *Posture and Pain.* Baltimore: Williams & Wilkins Co., 1952.

Kleinberg, Samuel, *Scoliosis.* Baltimore: Williams & Wilkins Co., 1951.

Lowman, Charles LeRoy, Claire Colestock, and Hazel Cooper, *Corrective Physical Education for Groups.* New York: A. S. Barnes & Co., 1928.

Lowman, Charles LeRoy, and Carl Haven Young, *Postural Fitness.* Philadelphia: Lea & Febiger, 1960.

Mathews, Donald K., Robert Kruse, and Virginia Shaw, *The Science of Physical Education for Handicapped Children.* New York: Harper & Row, Publishers, 1962.

Metheny, Eleanor, *Body Dynamics.* New York: McGraw-Hill Book Co., Inc., 1952.

Morrison, Whitelaw Reid, and Laurence B. Chenoweth, *Normal and Elementary Physical Diagnosis,* 5th ed. Philadelphia: Lea & Febiger, 1955.

Morton, Dudley J., *The Human Foot.* New York: Columbia University Press, 1935.

Morton, Dudley J., and Dudley Dean Fuller, *Human Locomotion and Body Form.* Baltimore: Williams & Wilkins Co., 1952.

Rasch, Philip J., and Roger K. Burke, *Kinesiology and Applied Anatomy,* 2nd ed. Philadelphia: Lea & Febiger, 1963.

Rathbone, Josephine Langworthy, *Corrective Physical Education,* 6th ed. Philadelphia: W. B. Saunders Co., 1959.

Stafford, George T., and Ellen Davis Kelly, *Preventive and Corrective Physical Education,* 3rd ed. New York: Ronald Press Co., 1958.

9

CONGENITAL AND PATHOLOGICAL CONDITIONS

Adaptations of man's movements are primarily the result of attempts to counteract the effects of the forces that affect his musculoskeletal system. These forces were previously defined as gravity, congenital and pathological conditions, and trauma or injury. One can readily observe the relationship between the force of gravity and the adaptations that the individual makes to resist its downward pull. The relationship between magnitude, direction, and point of application of force to a body segment and the resultant injury to the musculoskeletal system may be determined logically. However, musculoskeletal deformities whose origin is either congenital or pathological are not as easily understood.

One may be prone to assume that adaptations of man's movement must involve only the musculoskeletal system. This assumption is without basis. Although most of the factors that elicit movement adaptations do involve these systems, there are numerous pathological conditions capable of modifying or limiting one's movement patterns. Since the effects of movement are organismic rather than systemic, it is logical to assume that any marked abnormality in the structure or in the function of one anatomical system would bring about adaptations in the functions of the others. This assumption is based on the physiological interrelationship that exists between anatomic systems.

Those individuals whose physical condition prohibits their participation in the regular physical education program are considered to be physically handicapped. Children who are physically handicapped include those who are (1) orthopedically handicapped, or crippled by infection, congenital anomalies, and developmental or other crippling conditions; (2) visually handicapped whether blind or partially seeing; (3) aurally handicapped, including both deaf and hard of hearing; (4) cerebral palsied; and (5) those who have special health problems, including such conditions as asthma, cardiac disturbances, diabetes, epilepsy, and tuberculosis.

The physically handicapped individual is generally assigned to the adapted physical education program. Consequently, the physical educator is primarily concerned with the nature of the student's physical condition and its implications for his physical education. This chapter deals with specific congenital and acquired divergencies or disorders that are most likely to impair one's locomotion or health to the extent that he is unable to receive maximum benefit from participation in the regular physical education program. In addition to being unable to participate in the regular physical education program, many physically handicapped children require other specialized educational services. These services may include the utilization of modified methods of instruction, specially designed materials and equipment, and other services deemed necessary to meet the educational needs of these children.[1]

Such an educational program for those physically handicapped children who are unable to benefit from participation in the regular instructional program is often referred to as *special education*. Special education programs are commonly organized to provide (1) itinerant teachers; (2) remedial classes such as speech therapy, adapted physical education, sight-saving classes, and lip-reading; (3) special day classes—special classes for the handicapped in the same building or on the same campus of the regular school; (4) spe-

[1] James G. Dunkelberg, "Criteria for Evaluating Special Education Programs for Physically Handicapped Children" (Doctoral dissertation, University of California, Los Angeles, 1958), p. 6.

cial schools; (5) hospital classes; and (6) home teaching for those unable to go to school.

Children of a wide range of handicaps will be assigned to the adapted physical education classes. They may also require and may be receiving other special education services as well. Therefore, it is strongly recommended that all teachers of adapted physical education become familiar with the current literature and practices in the field of special education so that they may be able to provide a physical education program which will better meet the needs of these children.

Due to the nature of the divergencies which are to be discussed, it is imperative for the reader to remember that adapted physical education programming for the physically handicapped must be based on and guided by the physician's diagnosis and recommendations. Therefore, the implications concerning the various physically handicapping conditions must be understood to be general, and as such may provide a guide within which the specifics of the physician's recommendations can be implemented.

The two major classifications of physically handicapping conditions are *cogenital* and *acquired*. The word congenital means "born with." Thus, the anomalies are generally genetic or hereditary in origin. Congenital conditions are those anomalies or malformations which are present at birth. These may or may not be evident at birth. Acquired malformations are not present at birth. They are not traceable to a genetic or hereditary origin. Acquired abnormalities are primarily the result of disease and injury.

ORTHOPEDIC HANDICAPS

Orthopedic handicaps or crippling conditions are commonly classified as follows:

1. Crippling due to infection. This category includes joint tuberculosis, poliomyelitis, and osteomyelitis.

2. Cerebral palsy, including athetosis, ataxia, rigidity, spasticity, tremor, and variations of these manifestations of brain damage.

3. Crippling resulting from birth injury; Erb's palsy, bone fractures, and similar disorders.

4. Cardiovascular conditions of both congenital and acquired origins.

5. Congenital anomalies such as congenital amputation, congenital dislocation, clubfoot, torticollis, and spina bifida.

6. Traumatic crippling: amputation, fractures, and dislocations.

7. Tumors: bone tumors, bone cysts, and similar conditions.

8. Developmental conditions, including coxa plana, spinal osteochondritis, and Osgood-Schlatter disease.

9. Other conditions, such as multiple sclerosis and muscular dystrophy.

The following estimates of frequency of the various kinds of orthopedic handicaps in children who require special education services were derived from a survey by James G. Dunkelberg, Los Angeles State College:

Cerebral palsy	33%
Infection (musculoskeletal)	25%
Cardiovascular conditions	20%
Congenital anomalies	6%
Developmental conditions	6%
Trauma (musculoskeletal)	2%
Tumors (skeletal)	1%
Birth injury	1%
Other	6%

Of the various kinds of handicapping conditions, the majority are not correctable through use of exercise. Consequently, a large proportion of the children assigned to the adapted program will benefit most from a program of games and sports that have a carry-over value. This suggestion does not imply that exercise has no place in the program for physically handicapped children with permanent disabilities. However, it does mean that the emphasis is changed from that of correcting the condition to that of providing the student with the opportunity to achieve the maximum organic vigor or physical condition that his disability will permit. It is possible that some of the secondary changes affecting these children may respond favorably to exercise. Therefore, it is imperative that both the sports and the exercise phases of adapted physical education be made available to all physically handicapped children.

Talipes. A congenital malformation, either single or bilateral, in which the foot is fixed in any of the normal positions, such as plantar flexion, dorsiflexion, inversion, eversion, adduction, and abduction of the forefoot. Talipes implies that the fixed position involves both the ankle and foot. The usual classification of the fixed positions is as follows:

1. Talipes *equinus,* a position of plantar flexion. In the standing position, the body weight is borne on the toes.

2. Talipes *calcaneus,* a position of dorsiflexion. In the standing position, the weight is borne on the heel.

3. Talipes *valgus,* a position of eversion and abduction of the forefoot. In the standing position, the weight is borne on the medial or inner border of the foot (pronation).

4. Talipes *varus,* a position of inversion and adduction of the forefoot. In the standing position, the weight is borne on the lateral or outer border of the foot (supination).

A talipes condition rarely involves a single fixed foot or ankle position. It is usually a combination of a fixed ankle and a fixed foot position. The most common combination is one in which the ankle is fixed in plantar flexion and the foot is inverted and adducted. This condition, talipes *equinovarus,* is commonly referred to as a "clubfoot." It constitutes about 75 per cent of all talipes divergencies. Other combined fixed ankle-foot conditions are identified as (1) talipes *equinovalgus,* (2) talipes *calcaneovarus,* and (3) talipes *calcaneovalgus.*

Therapeutic exercise is usually of little value in the correction of a talipes divergency. However, exercise may be of value in increasing the strength of the stretched muscles and in increasing the flexibility of the ankle and foot. A program of general physical conditioning and adapted activities would be of benefit to the student. Because of the severe adaptations of the individual's weight bearing, sports and games that require extensive running, jumping, and kicking are contraindicated.

Erb's Palsy. A birth injury to the brachial plexus that results in paralysis of the upper limb. The injury is limited to the roots and trunk of the fifth and sixth cervical nerves. The individual loses the ability to abduct or externally rotate the upper limb at the shoulder and to supinate the forearm.

Therapeutic exercise is generally of little value in the correction of this condition. Exercises may, however, prevent the development of additional contractions by maintaining range of motion. Participation in sports and games that are within the limitations of this disability should be encouraged.

Congenital Dislocations. The prenatal displacement of one or more bones of a joint from the normal position. Generally, this condition affects the shoulder and the hip joints. Congenital dislocation and *dysplasia* of the hip may be unilateral or bilateral. Congenital dislocation of the hip is usually characterized by an upward and backward displacement of the head of the femur as well as by a thickening at the base of the acetabulum. The left hip is more frequently affected than is the right. The condition may be sex linked, because it affects more females than males. If the condition is unilateral, the individual has a lurching walk in which he appears to sink down on the affected side as weight is borne on that leg. All weight-bearing activities are contraindicated. Exercises for general conditioning may be used if they do not require standing. Sports and games which do not require standing and use of the lower limbs should be encouraged.

Coxa Vara and Coxa Valga. Normally, the angle between the neck of the femur and the shaft is approximately 135 degrees. A marked increase or decrease from this angle is abnormal.

Coxa vara is characterized by a decrease in the angle of the femur. The affected leg is usually shorter and its external rotation is limited. Coxa vara may occur as a congenital or as an acquired defect, the latter more commonly.

Coxa valga is characterized by an increase in the angle of the femur. The affected leg is usually longer. Rotation is limited. This condition is congenital.

Exercise for general conditioning is recommended. Prolonged weight bearing is contraindicated unless prescribed by the physician. Participation in sports and games which do not require excessive use of the legs is also recommended.

Osteochondrosis or Osteochondritis. A disease of children that affects the growth of epiphyseal centers in such a manner that inflammation of bone and cartilage occurs. It successively results in fragmentation and degeneration of the cartilage, which is followed by regeneration of the bone. Subsequently, there is a return to the normal hardness and strength of the involved surface. Various epiphyses may be involved, but certain ones seem to be more commonly affected. These are known by various names, and these names are dependent upon the site of involvement. Osteochondritis usually begins in children between four and twelve years of age and has a tendency to affect more boys than girls. The outstanding symptom is pain in the affected part, which causes a voluntary limitation of movement and a protective limp.

Coxa Plana. This condition—also known as *osteochondritis deformans juvenilis, Perthes' disease, Calve-Perthes' disease, Legg's disease,* and *Legg-Calve-Perthes disease*—is characterized by atrophy and rarefaction of the head of the femur. As a result, a shortened and thickened femoral neck, a broad, flat femoral head, and a flattening of the capital femoral epiphysis appear. The onset is insidious between the ages of five and twelve years. Since the disease is not primarily inflammatory, no fever or other evidence of inflammation is present. The presence of pain in the hip is the outstanding symptom; however, pain is frequently referred to the medial aspect of the knee since the obturator nerve may be involved.

Osgood-Schlatter Disease. This disease, also known as *osteochondritis dissecans,* is an inflammation or partial separation of the tibial tubercle. It is characterized by pain, tenderness on deep pressure, and swelling of the tibial tubercle. Pain becomes especially marked after physical activity, such as kicking or kneeling, or when the knee is forcibly extended against resistance. In the acute stage of the condition, therapeutic exercise is usually contraindicated.

Scheuermann's Disease. Also known as *osteochondritis deforman's juvenilis dorsi,* a condition confined to the vertebral epiphysis. It frequently results in producing kyphosis of the affected vertebrae.

Individuals with osteochondritis should avoid weight-bearing activities. General conditioning exercises are indicated. Special unilateral exercises may be used, because the contralateral effects of exercise may help to maintain the tone and strength of the affected limb. Sports and games appropriate to the individual's limitations are recommended.

Slipped Femoral Epiphysis. This condition closely resembles osteochondrosis. It results in a nontraumatic separation of the femoral head at the epiphysis and is often associated with children who are excessively obese, tall and thin, or who have recently experienced a period of rapid growth. The individual walks with the foot in a toed-out position as a result of external rotation of the thigh. Inward rotation, an early characteristic of the condition, is limited.

Sports and games requiring excessive use of the lower limbs and prolonged weight bearing are contraindicated. General conditioning is recommended. Exercises may also be used that will maintain the range of motion of the affected limb.

Spondylolisthesis. An anterior displacement of the fifth lumbar vertebra on the sacrum. This vertebra overhangs the brim of the pelvis and may cause pressure on the spinal nerves. About one in five persons has some congenital structural variation of the lumbosacral joint. The disability generally manifests itself as the child approaches puberty. The onset of the disease may be the result of some minor trauma. Consequently, all children with acute or exaggerated lordosis or sharp hyperextension at the lumbosacral junction should be closely scrutinized.

Due to the possibility of trauma's eliciting this divergency, the individual with an extreme lordotic curve of the lumbar spine should not engage in contact sports and gymnastics without medical approval. Heavy resistance exercises may also be contraindicated.

Brittle Bones. Also known as *osteogenesis imperfecta,* or *osteopsathyrosis.* A familial disease of the long bones characterized by abnormal brittleness leading to a history of numerous fractures, marked atrophy of the extremities, and the presence of a marked change in the anatomical characteristics of the limbs and joints. Vigorous physical activities, resistance exercises, and sports are contraindicated.

Spina Bifida. A congenital defect in which there is incomplete closure of the vertebral lamina and, occasionally, protrusion or herniation of the meninges of the spinal cord. This defect is most common in the lumbosacral area of the spine. Its characteristics include loss of tactile sensitivity of the legs, and incontinence. Physical activity, other than sedentary games, is contraindicated if a meningocele is present.

Skeletal Tuberculosis. A tubercular infection of the bones and joints. Usually, it develops insidiously during the first ten years of life. About one-half of all cases occur in the spine. The hip area is also very vulnerable to tubercular infection.

Pott's Disease. Also called *tuberculous spondylitis,* or tuberculosis of the spine, this disease is characterized by the development of an abnormal prominence at some level of the spine. This localized kyphosis usually occurs in the thoracic spine, but it can also occur in the cervical and lumbar regions of the spine. Vigorous physical activities are contraindicated.

Osteomyelitis. An inflammation of the bone caused by pyogenic (pus producing) bacteria, especially staphylococci and streptococci. It is frequently characterized by destruction of the bone. It is recurrent and usually involves several bones unless the initially infected bone is completely removed. It is seen most frequently in children who are between the ages of three and ten years. Vigorous physical activities are contraindicated.

Muscular Dystrophy. A crippling disease which mysteriously attacks the muscles. The disease usually affects the proximal muscles first, and a progressive wasting and weakness occurs. Eventually, the condition extends to practically all voluntary muscles of the body. The disease itself is not considered fatal, but the debility it causes makes slight illnesses extremely dangerous. The disease is characterized by four types. (1) *Pseudohypertrophic,* the most prevalent form, commences in childhood between the ages of three and ten. Its course is more rapid than that of any other type. It is considered to be hereditary in 35 per cent of the cases and it affects three times as many boys as girls. (2) *Juvenile form*—onset in childhood or adolescence—has a progression that is slower. Patients may reach middle age and boys and girls are affected equally. (3) *Facio-scapulo-humeral* affects young adults; attacks the facial muscles, the shoulders, and upper arms. (4) *Mixed types* is a combination of the aforementioned conditions; the onset of the disease may be between the ages of thirty and fifty. This type is not inherited and it can strike anyone. The course of the disease is rapid and is often terminal in five to ten years.

Exercise will not arrest the dystrophic process nor restore wasted muscles. However, general conditioning exercises may delay the stage of complete helplessness. Recreational games and sports are indicated when they are within the limitations of the physician's recommendations.

Multiple Sclerosis. A disease of the nervous system in which the nerve pathways have been damaged by the formation of patches of scar tissue in the central nervous system. The condition develops between the ages of ten and forty, and more males are affected than females. It develops gradually and becomes progressively worse over a period of years. There does not seem to be any hereditary factor involved.

Exercises aimed at neuromuscular reeducation are indicated. General conditioning exercises are of value in maintaining a high level of physical fitness or organic vigor. Recreational games and sports are of utmost importance in morale building and instilling the will to live.

Amputation. The removal, wholly or in part, of a limb or of a projecting process. Amputation may be indicated in the course of pathological processes such as gangrene or constriction. *Traumatic* amputation may result from an accident. *Surgical* amputation may be undertaken in order to remove a malignant tumor. *Congenital* amputation is the result of prenatal processes that may be either developmental or pathological in nature. It may also be due to genetic or hereditary factors.

The loss of a limb or a part thereof involves an irrevocable anatomical and physiological impairment of major proportions. The individual who has had an amputation may participate in any physical activity, exercise, game, or sport of which he is capable.

Wry Neck. Generally a congenital defect but may be induced by psychic stresses as a result of excessive emotional tensions. Because of muscular imbalance of the sternocleidomastoid muscles, the head is laterally flexed and rotated to one side. This condition is also referred to as *torticollis*.

The individual may participate in most games and sports. Exercise may be used to increase the strength of the lengthened muscle and thereby to increase the flexibility of the neck.

VISUAL HANDICAPS

It has been estimated that one in every four children has some sort of visual anomaly. The differentiation between "normal vision" and the various degrees of deviation is made on the basis of *visual acuity*.

The Partially Seeing

Generally, partially seeing children are defined as those with visual acuity of less than 20/70 or more than 20/200. This acuity is of the best eye after all necessary medical and surgical treatment has been given and compensating lenses have been provided. Hathaway[2] feels also that the individual must have a sufficient residue of sight to make it possible to use sight as the chief avenue of approach to the brain. She also includes those children whose visual deviations are such that they may benefit from the special educational services provided for the partially seeing. There were approximately 68,000 to 70,000 partially seeing children of pre-school and school age in the United States during 1955.[3] The following kinds of visual defects may be found among partially seeing children and are listed here in order of their frequency: (1) *refractive errors* (myopia, hyperopia); (2) *developmental anomalies* of structure (cataracts, albinism); (3) *defects of muscle function* (strabismus, nystagmus); and (4) *disease* or *defects* of the eye (caused by infection, injuries).

Children with these conditions require slight modifications of physical activity, games, and sports. Care should be used when the student must wear glasses. It is recommended that glass-guards be

[2] Winifred Hathaway, *Education and Health of the Partially Seeing Child,* 4th ed. (New York: Columbia University Press, 1959), p. 16.

[3] American Public Health Association Committee for Child Health, and the National Society for Prevention of Blindness, *Service for Children with Vision and Eye Problems* (New York: American Public Health Association, 1956).

worn. Due to the possibility of retinal detachment, students with high myopia should not be permitted to engage in contact sports.

The Blind

Those individuals whose vision affords them no practical value for the purposes of education, business, and activities of daily living are considered to be blind. However, any definition depends upon the purpose for which it is made. For educational purposes, a person is blind if his vision is so defective that he cannot be educated through visual methods. Or he is blind if he must be taught through his auditory and tactile senses. There is lack of evidence to substantiate the belief that because of blindness the individual gains in other senses. In terms of visual acuity, the educationally blind are those whose acuity is 20/200 or less in the best eye after all the necessary medical and surgical treatment and compensating measures have been provided. It is estimated that there are between 10,000 and 15,000 blind children of preschool and school age. Kerby[4] found that there were 7,000 blind children attending schools or classes for the blind in 1954–55. This number was increased to 13,491 by 1959. According to Kirk, this marked increase in blind children attending school was mainly attributed to the coming of school age of those children who had been made blind by *retrolental fibroplasia*.[5] The major causes in terms of frequency are (1) unspecified prenatal causes; (2) poisoning, including that of excessive oxygen; (3) heredity; (4) infectious disease, tumors, and injuries. After a decade of research, it was determined that the administration of an excessive amount of oxygen to premature children was causing a condition referred to as retrolental fibroplasia. This form of oxygen poisoning causes a complete detachment of the retina. This condition was nonexistent prior to 1938, and it had virtually disappeared by 1955. This case is an example of how a medical advance in one area can produce a handicapping condition that is otherwise unrelated.

[4] Edith Kerby, "Causes of Blindness in Children of School Age," *Sight Saving Review*, XXVIII (Spring 1958), 18–21.
[5] Samuel A. Kirk, *Educating Exceptional Children* (Boston: Houghton Mifflin Co., 1962), p. 215.

The blind may benefit from participation in a wide variety of physical education activities. However, the instructor must utilize the auditory and tactile senses in his instruction almost exclusively.

AURAL HANDICAPS

Individuals with aural handicaps may have difficulty in hearing, or they may not be able to hear at all. There are different degrees of hearing loss, which vary from a very slight loss for certain sounds to complete loss of hearing for all sounds. In addition to the degree of loss, the severity of the disability is influenced by the age for the onset of the impairment. The educational programs for children with aural handicaps differ according to the nature and extent of their hearing acuity. Therefore, it was imperative that standardized terminology be developed. The following classification was made at the Conference of Executives of American Schools for the Deaf:

The Deaf: Those in whom the sense of hearing is nonfunctional for the ordinary purposes of life. This group is made up of two distinct classes based entirely on the time the loss of hearing occurred. These include:
a. The congenitally deaf—those who were born deaf.
b. The adventitiously deaf—those who were born with normal hearing but in whom the sense of hearing became nonfunctional later through illness or injury.
The Hard of Hearing: Those in whom the sense of hearing, although defective, is functional with or without a hearing aid.[6]

Streng[7] has further classified the auditorily handicapped in accordance with the degree of hearing loss. For example, those students whose hearing loss is greater than 75 decibels even with amplification are unable to use hearing to understand language. They require specialized instruction in all areas. She classified these children for educational purposes as deaf. Auditory handicaps are also classified on the basis of cause as either *endogenous* or *exoge-*

[6] Committee on Nomenclature, Conference of Executives of American Schools for the Deaf, *American Annals of the Deaf,* LXXXIII (January 1938), 1–7.

[7] Alice Streng et al., *Hearing Therapy for Children,* 2nd ed. (New York: Grune & Stratton, Inc., 1958), pp. 164–165.

nous. Endogenous refers to hereditary causes, exogenous refers to accidents and diseases as causative factors. The most common exogenous causes are meningitis, scarlet fever, pneumonia, whooping cough, ear infections, and accidents that injure the ear. Estimates concerning the prevalence of impaired hearing range from 1.5 to 5 per, cent of the school-age population.

Individuals with moderate hearing losses are able to participate in the regular physical education program with little or no modification of the activities. For those students who are educationally deaf, the instructor must utilize the sense of vision in his instruction. The deaf child also requires physical education to develop or improve his balance.

CEREBRAL PALSY

The most simple—but somewhat misleading—definition of cerebral palsy is derived from the two words. "Cerebral" means brain and "palsy" means a motor disability; therefore, cerebral palsy means a condition resulting from damage or from a dysfunction of those portions of the brain that govern or control muscular function. The United Cerebral Palsy Association attempted to show the complex nature of this disability when it defined the condition as follows:

Cerebral palsy embraces the clinical picture created by injury to the brain, in which one of the components is motor disturbance. Thus, cerebral palsy may be described as a group of conditions, usually originating in childhood, characterized by paralysis, weakness, incoordination or any other aberration of motor function caused by pathology of the motor control center of the brain. In addition to such motor dysfunction, cerebral palsy may include learning difficulties, psychological problems, sensory defects, convulsive and behavioral disorders of organic origin.[8]

Motor dysfunction may involve different groups of muscles of one or more of the limbs. If only one limb is involved, the condition is called *monoplegia.* If both limbs on the same side are affected, it is called *hemiplegia.* If both of the lower limbs are involved, it is called *paraplegia.* When three of the limbs are affected, it is called *triplegia.* This condition usually involves both lower limbs and one

---

[8] The United Cerebral Palsy Research and Educational Foundation, *Program for Calendar Year 1958* (New York: The Foundation, 1958), p. 1.

upper limb. If all four limbs are involved, it is called *quadriplegia*. There are many times when the head and the trunk are also involved. Cerebral palsy takes different forms with different neuromotor involvements and characteristics. These are differentiated as *spasticity, athetosis, ataxia, tremor,* and *rigidity*. Furthermore, there are combinations of these called *mixed types*.

Spasticity is characterized by muscle stiffness in which the muscles remain in a state of tension. The normal muscular balance between agonist and antagonist is absent. Volitional movements tend to be jerky and uncontrolled as a result of spasmodic contraction of the muscles. They also evidence the "overflow" phenomenon which may manifest itself by participation of muscles not primarily concerned with the performance of the movement or skill. This syndrome may involve facial contortions, increased respiratory rate, and the production of guttural sounds. The stretch reflex is also a distinctive characteristic of this kind of cerebral palsy.

Athetosis is characterized by bizarre twisting, writhing muscular movements. Walking is characterized by a lurching and stumbling nonrhythmical pattern. Voluntary movements do not seem to follow any established sequence, and they are characterized by various uncontrolled movements.

Ataxia is characterized by impaired or lost kinesthetic sense and equilibrium. A person suffering from ataxia is very unsteady in his movements, walks with a high step, and frequently falls. The eyes are often uncoordinated, and *nystagmus*—jerky movements of the eyes—is common.

Tremor is characterized by slow, involuntary, rhythmic shaking or vibrating movements of an irregular nature. This condition may be present at rest, but usually is most marked when voluntary muscle action is attempted.

Rigidity is characterized by interference with postural tone as the result of simultaneous contractions of the agonistic and antagonistic muscles. There is more of a diminished or limited amount of movement rather than abnormal movement.

Deaver[9] and Rusk[10] estimated that there is one child born

[9] G. G. Deaver, *Cerebral Palsy: Methods of Evaluation and Treatment*, Rehabilitation Monograph IX (Institute of Physical Medicine and Rehabilitation, New York University Medical Center, 1955).

[10] Howard A. Rusk, *Rehabilitation Medicine* (St. Louis: C. V. Mosby Co., 1958), p. 409.

with cerebral palsy approximately every two hundred live births, or that a cerebral-palsied or brain-injured child is born every 53 minutes.

These children require special adaptations of most of the games and sports which comprise the physical education program. Special attention should be placed on the development of relaxation and coordination. Fine and rapid muscular movements are extremely difficult. These children will exaggerate their muscular dysfunction as a result of increased tension. When introducing any new activity or new equipment, allow the child enough time to become acquainted with it. This procedure will avoid the development of increased tension that will limit the child's ability to perform the desired skill or movement.

SPECIAL ILLNESS PROBLEMS

Children with special illness problems are those whose weakened physical condition renders them relatively inactive or that requires special health precautions in school. They may have cardiac anomalies, epilepsy, diabetes, asthma, or tuberculosis. They have been described as "delicate" or as "children with low vitality."

Cardiac Anomalies. The two main kinds of cardiac disturbances may be classified as *functional* and *organic*. Functional disturbances are those that do not involve any structural changes in the heart. Organic disturbances refer to a permanent malformation of the cardiac structure. Some children are born with congenital organic disturbances. The most common cause of acquired heart disabilities is rheumatic fever. This disease often strikes school-aged children, and it may or may not result in organic involvement. Regardless of the nature or cause of the disturbance, the physical educator is primarily interested in the effect of the disability upon the individual's physical activity. The physician is primarily concerned with the classification of the cardiac disturbance or heart damage in terms of functional capacity. The New York Heart Association has developed a guide for understanding and controlling the activity of cardiac pupils by functional capacity and therapeutic classification:[11]

Functional Capacity

Class I. Patients with a cardiac disorder without limitation of physical activity. Ordinary physical activity causes no discomfort.

Class II. Patients with a cardiac disorder with slight to moderate limitation of physical activity. Ordinary physical activity causes no discomfort.

Class III. Patients with a cardiac disorder with moderate to marked limitation of physical activity. Less than ordinary physical activity causes discomfort.

Class IV. Patients with a cardiac disorder unable to carry on any physical activity without discomfort.

Therapeutic Classification

Class A. Patients with a cardiac disorder whose ordinary physical activity need not be restricted.

Class B. Patients with a cardiac disorder whose ordinary physical activity need not be restricted, but who should be advised against unusually severe or competitive efforts.

Class C. Patients with a cardiac disorder whose ordinary physical activity should be moderately restricted and whose more than strenuous habitual efforts should be discontinued.

Class D. Patients with a cardiac disorder whose physical activity should be markedly restricted.

Class E. Patients with a cardiac disorder who should be at complete bed rest, confined to bed or chair.

It is estimated that between 10 and 15 per cent of the students enrolled in special education classes have heart conditions. It is also estimated that approximately 20,000 new cases of rheumatic fever occur each year. About 70 per cent of the children who are afflicted with this condition between the ages of five and ten suffer some degree of heart damage.

The energy output should be kept minimal for students with heart disturbances. These students should avoid dyspnea (labored,

---

[11] New York Heart Association, "The Classification of Patients with Diseases of the Heart," *Nomenclature and Criteria for the Diagnosis of Diseases of the Heart and Blood Vessels,* 5th ed. (New York: The Association, 1953).

difficult breathing) and fatigue but may participate in all activities within their limitations.

Poliomyelitis. This disease is a virus infection that attacks the central nervous system. Damage or destruction occurs in the motor cells of the gray matter in the anterior horn of the spinal cord. The voluntary muscles innervated by these motor cells become paralyzed, atrophic, and flaccid. Poliomyelitis, also known as infantile paralysis, accounted for the largest single enrollment of children in special education classes in 1939–1942. However, with the discovery of the Salk and the Sabine vaccines, the incidence of paralytic polio has decreased in the United States. With the development of the live, attenuated poliomyelitis vaccine in pill form and the Salk vaccine injection, it is hoped that these preventive measures will eventually make poliomyelitis as infrequent as smallpox and diphtheria.

Individuals with poliomyelitis may receive benefits from an appropriate exercise program. The program should be designed to increase endurance, strength, and flexibility. Participation in selected and modified games and sports should also be of value to the individual during his leisure.

Asthma. The cause of asthma is not known, but there is some evidence that it may be psychologically induced. It is generally thought to be the result of some allergic phenomenon. It is characterized by recurrent attacks of labored breathing due to an obstruction of the bronchial tubes. As a result of reflex spasms of the bronchial musculature, accompanied by edema of the mucous membrane, the student with asthma may have an obstruction of the air flow to the lungs. As an asthma attack continues, thick mucus fills the bronchial tubes. The patient produces a characteristic wheezing as he exhales.

Although the individual would benefit from a general conditioning program, particular care must be taken to avoid dyspnea and fatigue. There is some belief that breathing exercises may help by restoring the asthmatic's confidence, and this may lessen his fear during an attack.

Diabetes Mellitus. This disorder is a complex hereditary metabolic disease in which the ability to oxidize carbohydrates is faulty.

This is due to the diminished production of insulin secreted by the islands of Langerhans in the pancreas. The disease is characterized by an increase of sugar in the blood (hyperglycemia) and an excretion of sugar in the urine (glycosuria). Through the injection of insulin, the carbohydrate tolerance of the diabetic is increased. Consequently, the individual may overindulge in exercise. This may bring about hypoglycemia—a sudden reduction of the blood-sugar level below normal. If this condition occurs, the diabetic needs to ingest carbohydrates.

The diabetic should engage only in sports and games that do not require physical contact because of the possibility of his receiving an abrasion or laceration and because of the diabetic's susceptibility to infection. He should be encouraged to engage in standardized amounts of physical activity, and he should participate daily to establish a uniform metabolic base. For this reason, exercises for general conditioning and endurance are of definite value.

Dysmenorrhea. This condition of painful or difficult menstruation may have a number of physiological and psychological causes. Dysmenorrhea may be caused by congestion of the blood in the abdominal cavity, lack of exercise, fatigue, poor posture, or by structural and organic abnormalities. However, there is a close relationship between emotional states and the events associated with menstruation. Adolescent girls who have not succeeded in establishing mature attitudes toward menstruation may experience "premenstrual tension" or incapacitating dysmenorrhea. Their reactions to menses may include such symptoms as anxiety, unhappiness, depression, and moderate discomfort to severe pain. Dysmenorrhea may occur at the beginning of the menstrual cycle or before the flow is fully established. It is characterized by uterine cramps, backache, leg aches, and nausea.

Certain exercises have been shown to be of value in preventing or lessening the severity of dysmenorrhea. Exercises that increase lumbosacral flexibility, such as the Billig's exercise,[12] are recommended for those cases in which the student complains of backache and leg aches.

---

[12] Harvey E. Billig, Jr., and Evelyn Lowendahl, *Mobilization of the Human Body* (Stanford, Calif.: Stanford University Press, 1949), pp. 31–35.

Hernia. A protrusion of a loop of an organ or tissue through an abnormal opening. Such protrusions may occur at many different places within the body. *Abdominal* hernias, the protrusion of some internal structure (viscera) through an abnormal opening in the abdominal wall, are the most frequent types. The names of the various abdominal hernias are taken from their locations. For example, an *umbilical* hernia indicates that it involves the umbilicus, and the *inguinal* hernia occurs at the inguinal canal. The latter type is the most common. An inguinal hernia results from the protrusion of the intestine into the inguinal canal. The canal's internal opening, the internal abdominal ring, fails to close completely. As a result, a weak place is formed in the abdominal wall. Therefore, undue weakness of the abdominal wall, as the result of underdeveloped abdominal muscles, general muscular debility, injury, or any unusual or sudden increase or rise in the intra-abdominal pressure will predispose or may cause a hernia. Vigorous physical activity—such as lifting heavy weights, wrestling, or similar activities—in which the individual exerts strenuous pressure or force with the epiglottis closed, causes a significant increase of the intra-abdominal pressure. It is important, therefore, to instruct students not to hold their breath with the mouth closed or to close the glottis while lifting heavy weights.

Any activity that will significantly increase the intra-abdominal pressure is contraindicated for those with an unrepaired hernia. In severe cases, running may cause herniation of the viscera through the abdomimal wall.

Epilepsy. This condition is not a specific disease, but rather a syndrome, or series of symptoms, which is characterized by chronic convulsions or seizures. The seizures differ in type and in nature of the form, and in intensity of the loss of consciousness. A seizure may involve a convulsive jerking of parts of the body, emotional outbursts, and periods of mental confusion or amnesia. There are three major types of epilepsy that are of particular concern to the physical educator. These are (1) major motor seizure including *grand mal,* (2) minor motor seizure including *petit mal,* and (3) psychomotor seizures. The grand mal is a true convulsion, in which the individual falls and loses consciousness. The period of attack lasts from two to five minutes. It is followed by a period of mental confusion, disorientation, dullness, fatigue, and headache.

The individual who has this type of seizure often experiences an aura or sensation, which may be motor, sensory, or visceral. The sensation tends to remain constant for that individual. Petit mal is characterized by transient periods of unconsciousness that last approximately five to twenty seconds. During this time, the patient has a blank, staring expression. He may become immobile, or he may demonstrate rhythmic movements such as blinking, nodding the head, and twitching of the limbs and trunk. There is no general convulsion of the body. The patient does not fall, but he may drop objects that he holds in his hands. He may experience from one to a hundred or more seizures in a day.

Psychomotor epilepsy is characterized by a period of amnesia. The symptoms are extremely varied. The manifestations may be chiefly motor, in the form of automatisms such as rubbing and masticatory movements, or they may be chiefly psychic in the form of confused, dreamlike states, hallucinations, and temper outbursts. Duration of the seizure may vary from a few minutes to several hours. Psychomotor epilepsy is uncommon in children.

The major problem confronting the epileptic, in terms of his physical activity, is that of losing consciousness. Consequently, he should not be permitted to work with gymnastic equipment or to engage in other activities in which he is not in contact with the floor. Participation in physical activity may be of potential value for the epileptic student, however, because the incidence of seizures is often lessened for the epileptic while he is engaging in vigorous neuromuscular activity.[13] Generally, the epileptic should not be permitted alone in swimming pools because of the possible loss of consciousness. But, under close supervision and using the "buddy system," he may benefit from swimming instruction. Thus, he will be able to use his "life saving" skill in an emergency situation.

Selected References

Cozen, Lewis, *Office Orthopedics*. Philadelphia: Lea & Febiger, 1959.

Gallagher, J. Roswell, *Medical Care of the Adolescent*. New York: Appleton-Century-Crofts, Inc., 1960.

[13] Wayne C. McKinney, "A Study of the Problem of the Epileptic Student in Physical Education" (unpublished research, Department of Physical Education, Long Beach State College, 1959).

Green, Morris, and Julius B. Richmond, *Pediatric Diagnosis*. Philadelphia: W. B. Saunders Co., 1955.

Hathaway, Winifred, *Education and Health of the Partially Seeing*, 4th ed. New York: Columbia University Press, 1959.

Kasch, Fred W., "The Exercise Tolerance of Normal Children and Those with Congenital Heart Disease." Paper presented to Research Section, Convention of the California Association for Health, Physical Education and Recreation, San Diego, 1962.

Kirk, Samuel A., *Educating Exceptional Children*. Boston: Houghton Mifflin Co., 1962.

Mayer, D. McCullagh, and Wilson A. Swanker, *Anomalies of Infants and Children*. New York: McGraw-Hill Book Co., Inc., 1958.

Streng, Alice, et al., *Hearing Therapy for Children*, 2nd ed. New York: Grune & Stratton, Inc., 1958.

10

TRAUMATIC
MUSCULOSKELETAL
CONDITIONS

Trauma is an injury caused by some form of external force. Traumas may result from a wide variety of causes. Those injuries most frequently seen in the adapted physical education class are typical of the injuries received in contact sports. These injuries are often received by the athlete while he is in an awkward or unprotected position. The students with traumatic disabilities that are encountered in adapted physical education classes usually have damaged the musculoskeletal system. Generally, the mechanism involved in the injury consists of the part being either *compressed* or *elongated*. Compression injuries are often either soft-tissue contusions or fractures. Elongation injuries usually involve stretching or tearing of connective tissue or muscle fibers.

Individuals with acute or chronic traumatic musculoskeletal conditions are frequently assigned to the adapted physical education class. The benefits of exercise or physical activity have application to both of these injury states. Usually, however, the acute phase of the injury has subsided before the individual is referred to the adapted physical education class. The task of the adapted physical education teacher becomes one of following the medical recommendation by administering therapeutic exercises and other forms of physical activity to aid in the rehabilitation of the individual. The factors to be developed through this program are strength, endurance, flexibility, and skill. A discussion of these factors is given in detail in Chapter 11.

Musculoskeletal injuries may be classified as *sprains, strains, dislocations,* and *fractures.* Sprains are by far the most frequent injury seen in the adapted physical education class. Therefore, much attention should be directed toward proper rehabilitative procedures for this condition. Strains, dislocations, and fractures, although less frequent, constitute another large proportion of injuries requiring therapeutic exercises for the proper recovery of function. Understanding the mechanism or the causative factors of each injury, the effect of the injury upon the individual, and specific implications for programming is required of the adapted physical education teacher.

A sprain is an injury to *ligamentous* tissue. Ligaments function to hold bones together to form joints. Ligaments are also structures to limit joint movement. Movement is performed by the muscles, which act upon the joints via their tendinous attachments. Injury to ligaments occurs when the joint is forced beyond a position normally held by the ligaments. Ligaments are generally non-elastic and, therefore, either stretch or tear when violent force causes the joint to be separated beyond its normal limits.

A strain is an injury that results in damage to *muscle.* This trauma is usually manifested by a tearing of the tendon or muscle fiber. From a functional viewpoint, the muscle fibers and the tendon that attaches the muscle fibers to other structures actually form a unit. Therefore, the term "strain" indicates an injury to one or more of the structures. A common site of the injury is the junction of the muscle fibers and the tendon. Severe strains in the belly of a muscle are usually called "pulled muscles."

A dislocation occurs when the *articular surfaces* of a joint are completely separated. Many severe sprains are, in reality, dislocations in which the joint surfaces have realigned themselves to their original position. If the bones remain separated, the injury is a dislocation. A partial separation of the joint surfaces is known as a *subluxation*. The tissues injured in a dislocation often include muscles, ligaments, and the joint capsule lining—the synovial membrane, nerves, and blood vessels that supply the area.

The application of medically supervised therapeutic exercise to help restabilize joints that have been dislocated is an important aspect of adapted physical education. Properly applied exercise aids in the prevention of recurrent dislocations. Also, strength-developing exercises may be recommended to bring the surrounding musculature to an optimum state for surgery.

A fracture is a *break* in a bone, in which the continuity of the bone's surfaces is disrupted. Fractures in the area of joints often involve the connective tissues that surround the joint. Associated injuries may involve sprains, strains, and dislocations. Some of the combinations of two or more of these have been named after the person who first described the condition. For example, the *Pott's fracture* of the ankle involves a chip fracture of the medial malleolus and a fracture of the lower end of the fibula, usually with an associated dislocation of the ankle joint.

Since the treatment of fractures usually consists of immobilization of the part for rather long periods of time, the prevention of atrophy of the muscle is necessary. *Muscle setting*—to tense the muscle—is often recommended to counteract this tendency. Once the cast has been removed, the need for strength, endurance, and flexibility must be met through properly applied exercise. Rehabilitation of these disabilities should be a major function of the adapted physical education class in order to return the individual to his maximum physical potential.

A selected number of frequently encountered traumatic musculoskeletal conditions are presented in the following pages. The students with the injuries discussed are usually referred to the adapted physical education class by the orthopedic physician. The high incidence of traumatic musculoskeletal conditions seen in the adapted physical education class requires the teacher to have a thorough knowledge and understanding of the mechanism of the injury and the implications for programming. Obviously, not all of the musculoskeletal disabilities that may occur can be presented here. Further reference should be made to the standard texts on the subject that are listed in the Appendix.

Most of the important anatomical structures that are related to the injuries illustrated and discussed in this chapter are described in Chapter 6 under the heading "Musculoskeletal Movement."

THE ANKLE

Sprain

Mechanism of the Injury. Sprains of the ankle usually involve extremes of movement of either *inversion* or *eversion*. The *inversion sprain* is the most common of these two. The most frequent cause of this injury is excessive pressure on the foot when the sole of the foot is turned inward. The typical position of the inversion sprain is illustrated in Figure 10.1. When the weight of the body falls directly over the point indicated at A, a number of ligamentous and other structures may be injured. The three ligaments most often involved in such injuries are indicated: B, anterior tibiofibular; C, anterior talofibular; and D, calcaneofibular. Although authorities disagree about which of these is injured most frequently, it can be safely stated that one or more of them will be involved in inversion sprains.

Sprains that occur when the ankle is in an everted position are seen much less frequently than are inversion sprains. *Eversion sprains* primarily involve the deltoid ligament—the medial collateral ligament of the ankle. The deltoid ligament, however, has such great tensile strength that it may resist the injuring force and pull off part of the end of the medial malleolus, causing a chip fracture in that area. Chip fractures are not uncommonly associated with severe sprains to either the medial or the lateral aspects of the ankle. If a fracture does occur, the implications for adapted physical education are the same as for other types of fractures. But, in the case of a ligament injury, it should be remembered that once ligaments are elongated by stretching or tearing they will not return to their original length except through surgical intervention. Fortunately, the trend is toward immediate immobilization of severely torn ligaments and their associated structures. This practice seems to be lessening the high incidence of instability due to elongated, improperly healed ligaments.

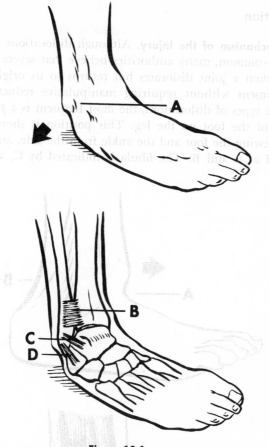

Figure 10.1

Implications for Programming. The students with traumatic musculoskeletal conditions who are referred to the adapted physical education class will be sent there after the acute stage of the injury has subsided. However, if the injury is still acute, special recommendations may be made for such activity as range-of-motion or flexibility exercises. The recommendation generally given for chronic or recurrent ankle sprains calls for strength- and endurance-developing exercises to help restabilize the joint. Refer also to the ankle-exercise routine presented in Chapter 12.

Dislocation

Mechanism of the Injury. Although dislocations of the ankle are not common, many authorities believe that severe sprains may result when a joint dislocates but returns to its original position of alignment without requiring manipulative reduction. Of the different types of dislocations, the most frequent is a *posterior projection* of the foot on the leg. This position is shown in Figure 10.2. Viewing the foot and the ankle from the side, an indentation is noted at A and B. The fibula is indicated by C, and the talus

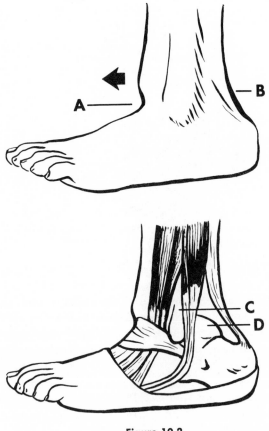

Figure 10.2

is indicated by D. Since two peroneal tendons and two long flexor tendons of the foot pass behind the malleoli on both sides of the ankle, there is a tendency for the bones of the leg to be forced forward when the individual is standing on the ball of the foot. If extreme downward force is exerted while in this position, there would be a tendency for these tendons to dislocate, in effect, the ankle. There is little muscular support from the front to prevent this action. Numerous ligaments are attached in such a way that they resist this force; but if the action is violent, there is a tendency for the ankle to dislocate. In any case, severe damage is sustained that could result in a dislocation.

Implications for Programming. Since dislocations of the ankle result in damage to the ligaments, which maintain normal joint relationships, the rehabilitation program in adapted physical education would be similar to that recommended for severe ankle sprains. Again, the purpose is to help restabilize the joint through strength-developing exercises. (See the ankle-exercise routine in Chapter 12.)

Fracture

Mechanism of the Injury. A Pott's fracture is illustrated in Figure 10.3. Indicated at A is an indentation in the medial side of the ankle that has been caused by a chip fracture in that area. A Pott's fracture involves a fracture of the lower end of the fibula (B), and the deltoid ligament (D) pulls away part of the medial malleolus (C) from the tibia. This fracture is seen in contact sports, particularly in football.

Implications for Programming. Recommended exercises are similar to those for fractures that are placed in immobilizing casts. Since inactivity usually results in atrophy and adaptive shortening of muscles, strengthening and stretching are necessary. Referral should be made to the ankle-exercise routine described in Chapter 12.

THE KNEE

Mechanism of Injury. The arrows in Figure 10.4 indicate the direction-of-force that usually causes stretching or tearing of the

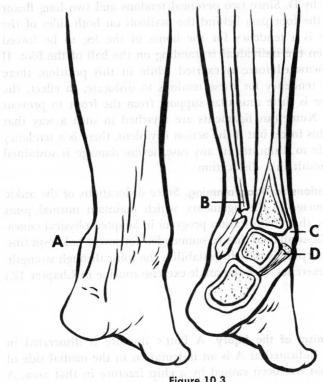

Figure 10.3

medial collateral ligament—the most frequently injured knee ligament. The medial collateral ligament (A) is attached to the
meniscus (interarticular or semilunar) cartilage (B) by fibrous connective tissue. Note that there is no attachment between the lateral
meniscus and the lateral collateral ligament (C). Since the meniscus
is attached to the superior surface of the head of the tibia and also
attached to the medial collateral ligament, a blow to the lateral
side of the knee stretches the medial collateral ligament, which in
turn may dislodge the medial meniscus from the head of the tibia.
Therefore, if a severe medial collateral ligament injury occurs, an
associated injury to the medial meniscus may be anticipated.

Occasionally, the knee will be hit from the medial side. A
tearing of the lateral collateral ligament may be expected. How-

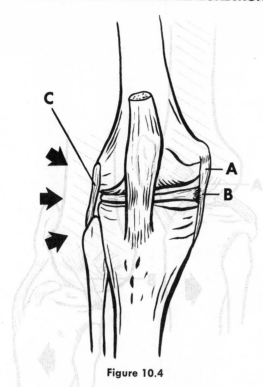

Figure 10.4

ever, fewer lateral meniscus injuries result than medial meniscus injuries. This results from the fact that the lateral meniscus does not attach to the lateral collateral ligament.

The second most frequently injured ligaments of the knee are the *cruciates*. Of the two cruciates, *anterior* and *posterior*, the anterior cruciate is damaged more often than is the posterior cruciate. The mechanism whereby these ligaments are torn is shown in Figure 10.5. The anterior cruciate ligament is indicated at A. The posterior cruciate ligament is indicated at B. If the head of the tibia is forcefully driven backward in the direction of the arrow when the femur is fixed, the posterior cruciate may be injured. On the other hand, if the tibia is driven forward when the femur is fixed, the anterior cruciate ligament may be torn. Anterior cruciate injuries in sports occur most often when the knee is partially flexed

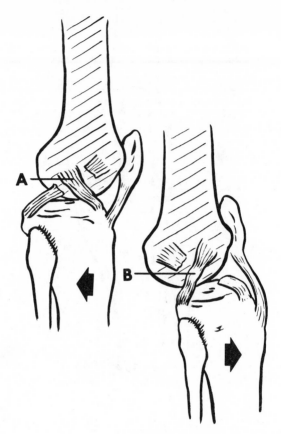

Figure 10.5

during running at the same time that another individual falls across the back of the leg below the knee. This action drives the head of the tibia toward the ground. This mechanism in football is called "clipping." Anterior cruciate injuries occur very frequently as a result of "clipping."

Implications for Programming. Strength-developing exercises for the prevention of knee injuries in sports are being widely adopted. Knowledge of specific exercises for stabilizing the knee joint is extremely important. The muscles or muscle groups involved at this joint are described in Chapter 6. All three muscle groups about the knee should be strengthened for optimum results. A knee-exercise routine appears in Chapter 12.

In *isotonic* exercises, the increases in bulk (hypertrophy) and in strength are closely related. An increase in one will usually follow the other. During the application of restabilizing, strength-developing exercises, it is advisable to measure the circumference of the thigh and that of the calf of the injured leg for comparison with the uninjured. A continuous recording of these measurements will provide evidence of progress, and it can also offer a means of motivating the student.

In order to compare the relative strengths of the knee extensors of both legs—if pain permits—the individual may sit on a table with the backs of his knees contacting its edge. While the knees are extended, the tester applies equal pressure just above the ankles to both legs. The weaker of the two muscle groups will "give" first. This procedure is helpful in making a gross determination of comparative muscular strength. When the strength is approximately even, both limbs should be exercised against progressively increasing resistance.

THE HIP

Mechanism of Injury. Because the hip is structured primarily for weight bearing, it is relatively stable. This stability comes from the deep articulation of the *head* of the femur with the *acetabulum* of the innominate bone, strong ligaments, and heavy musculature surrounding the joint. Due to the nature of the joint, dislocations are much less frequent than fractures. Most fractures occur to the neck of the femur and are, in many cases, the results of automobile accidents. Fractures of the hip are common in individuals over sixty years of age since there is a tendency for the bone to become abnormally porous in the aging process.

A dislocation of the hip is shown in Figure 10.6. The head of the femur (A) is completely separated from the acetabulum (B). Occasionally in a dislocation of this type, the *ligamentum teres* (C) may be torn or completely severed. The blood supply to the

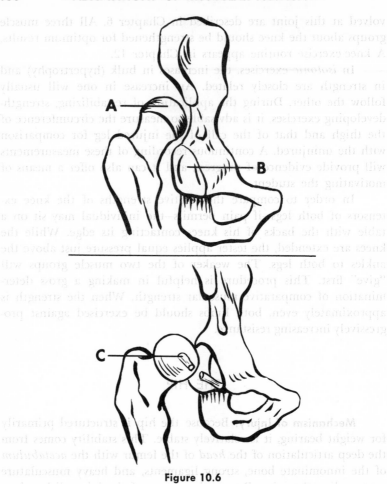

Figure 10.6

head of the femur runs through this ligament. Therefore, injury to the teres ligament may result in disintegration of the head of the femur.

Implications for Programming. Students with hip injuries are not too common in the adapted physical education program. Other involvements of the hip, for which exercise may be recommended by the physician, include such conditions as *Perthes' disease* and *adolescent coxa vara.*

Increasing the flexibility after some form of disability is a major purpose of therapeutic exercises in the adapted physical education program. Exercises for the hip are described in Chapter 12.

THE BACK

Mechanism of Injury. Traumatic musculoskeletal conditions of the spine usually present a complex picture. A majority of the structures that compose the back may be traumatized. In addition, referred pain may exist in areas that were not actually involved in the specific injury. Therefore, considerable difficulty arises in accurately determining the nature of the injury. Traumatic disabilities may be either sprains, strains, or fractures. Along with these injuries, *compression herniations* of the *intervertebral discs* may occur. Some medical authorities believe that most back pain is related to some form of damage to the discs. Others are of the opinion that only a small proportion of back problems result from disc injuries.[1] Although traumatic injury is a cause of back disability, Kraus and Raab[2] feel that over 80 per cent of lower-back pains are a result of physical inactivity. They stress the use of preventive and therapeutic exercise for disabilities of the back.

A median section of the lumbar spine is shown in Figure 10.7. The spinous process (A), the pedicle (B), and the body (C) of the vertebra are indicated. A normal intervertebral disc with its anulus fibrosus (D) and its nucleus pulposus (E) is indicated. The nucleus pulposus is a semifluid material and the anulus fibrosus is a fibrocartilaginous capsule. Trauma which forces the bodies of the vertebrae together, especially when the lumbar curvature is reversed, may force the nucleus pulposus through the anulus fibrosus and cause pressure on the posterior longitudinal ligament (F) of the spine. This posterior herniation is often called a "slipped disc." This condition is illustrated at G. Protrusion of the disc in this area places pressure on the nerve roots, which may, in turn, result in pain in the lower back and legs. The nucleus pulposus protrud-

---

[1] J. G. P. Williams, *Sports Medicine* (London: Edward Arnold (Publishers) Ltd., 1962), p. 189.

[2] Hans Kraus and Wilhelm Raab, *Hypokinetic Disease* (Springfield, Ill.: Charles C Thomas, 1961), p. 13.

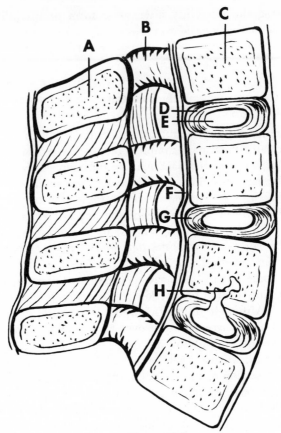

Figure 10.7

ing into the spongy part of the vertebral body is illustrated at H.

The mechanism involved in many back injuries caused by lifting is related to an increase in the hydraulic pressure of the nucleus pulposus.[3] If an individual attempts to lift a weight with the lumbar spine in a position that places undue pressure on the anterior portion of the disc (decreased curvature), the disc may herniate posteriorly. When a quick motion is exerted at the start

[3] Jay J. Keegan, "Alterations of the Lumbar Curve Related to Posture and Seating," *Journal of Bone and Joint Surgery*, XXXV-A, No. 3 (July 1953), 589–603.

of lifting an object, the hydraulic pressure within the intervertebral disc increases. With a greatly increased pressure, severe injury can occur even though the weight lifted is relatively light. The position just described is sometimes called the "7" position, because bending at the hips with the knees extended resembles the number seven. In order to avoid extreme reversal of the lumbar curve and to place less strain on the long strap-like extensor muscles which run from the base of the skull to the sacrum, the knees should be bent before lifting. This precaution releases the pull from the hamstring muscles since the hamstrings have a two-joint action crossing both the hip and knee joints in back. In this position, with the tension taken off the hamstrings, the lumbar spine is allowed to assume a more normal curvature. The weight should be lifted with the knee extensors rather than with the back extensors. The starting position for lifting a weight with the knee extensors rather than the back extensors has been called the "4" position, because it resembles the number four. Many potential injuries may be avoided through proper lifting mechanics.

Along with the compression injuries in which the intervertebral discs may be damaged, the body of a vertebra will fracture occasionally. Fortunately, these injuries are uncommon. A compression fracture of a vertebral body is indicated at A in Figure 10.8. A chip fracture of the vertebral body is indicated at B. Injuries of this type are found more frequently in the cervical area than in other vertebrae in the spinal column. Fractures in which the spinous and transverse processes become detached from the vertebrae are the most common types of athletic injuries to the spinal column. A fracture to the spinous process (C) and transverse process (D) is shown in Figure 10.8. Injuries to these processes may result from violent activity in which the muscles pulling on the bone actually cause the fracture.

Implications for Programming. Individuals with traumatic back disabilities often comprise a large portion of those individuals who require therapeutic exercise in the adapted physical education class. Although there is a wide variety of difference in the injuries received, the exercise recommendations for back disabilities will be quite similar. Reference is made to Chapter 12 for the routine of exercises for back disabilities.

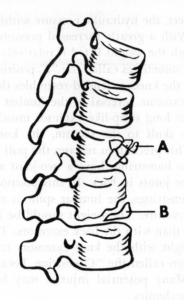

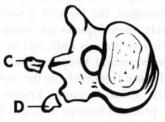

Figure 10.8

THE SHOULDER

Mechanism of Injury. In the general area of the shoulder, three joints must be considered. These are the gleno-humeral, acromio-clavicular, and the sterno-clavicular joints. Injury to the acromio-clavicular joint ranks first in order of frequency, followed by the gleno-humeral and the sterno-clavicular joints. Injuries in this area may involve spraining of ligaments, straining of muscle and con-nective tissue, and a dislocation of any of these three joints. Since a

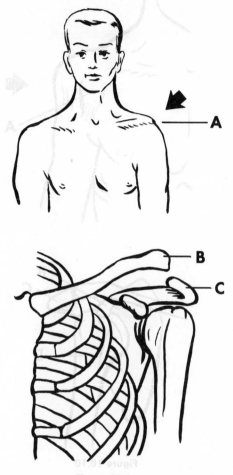

Figure 10.9

dislocation is defined as the complete separation of the surfaces of
a joint, the injury illustrated in Figure 10.9 is a dislocation. However, subluxations or partial dislocations of the acromio-clavicular
joints are called *separations*. This terminology is used in order to
differentiate between injuries to these two joints and to the gleno-
humeral joint. When it is said that an individual has a dislocation
of the shoulder, reference is made to a dislocation only at the gleno-

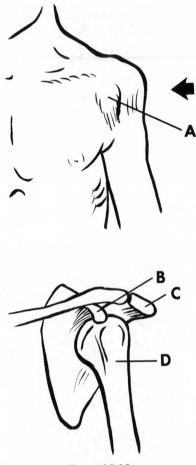

Figure 10.10

humeral joint. A shoulder separation at the acromio-clavicular joint is commonly referred to as a *shoulder point*. This injury may be caused by the individual's falling directly on the point of the shoulder or by breaking a fall with the arm extended. The injury shown in Figure 10.9 is considered to be a separation of the acromio-clavicular joint. A projection of the clavicle is pointed out at A. The clavicle is shown at B. The letter C shows the acromion process with which the clavicle articulates to form the acromio-clavicular joint.

A dislocation of the gleno-humeral joint is shown in Figure 10.10. Viewing the shoulder from the front, an indentation of the deltoid muscle is indicated by the arrow. A protrusion of the head of the humerus can usually be seen in the area indicated at A. The head of the humerus (D) is usually lodged in a position under the coracoid process (B) and the acromion process (C). The head of the humerus becomes prominent. This is called a subcoracoid dislocation of the humerus. Dislocations may also occur with the humeral head posterior to the scapula or inferior to the glenoid fossa of the scapula. The dislocation is brought about with the humerus at least at shoulder level while being externally rotated.

With the exception of fractures of the clavicle, fractures in the shoulder area are infrequent. Falling on the tip of the shoulder or with the arm outstretched may result in a clavicular fracture. Once the fracture has healed, rehabilitative exercises are usually indicated to overcome weaknesses due to the period of inactivity following the injury.

Implications for Programming. The gleno-humeral joint of the shoulder depends largely upon muscular function to maintain its integrity. Since dislocations of this joint are frequent, developing the musculature around the joint becomes a major task in the adapted physical education program. Once a dislocation of the shoulder joint has occurred, recurrences of the injury may progressively increase. In order to prevent these recurrences, a judiciously applied therapeutic exercise routine is extremely important. A routine of shoulder exercises is presented in Chapter 12.

One major precaution must be taken in relation to exercise for recurrent shoulder dislocations. The individual must never be allowed to exercise with the humerus at shoulder level or above, and with the arm in an externally rotated position. For example, if the individual should attempt to press a barbell over his head and allow the weight to move slightly posterior to his line of gravity, the chances of a recurrent dislocation would be greatly increased. Experience indicates that this mechanism does happen. Every attempt should be made to inform the student of this possibility. Furthermore, close supervision is required to see that such an exercise is not attempted.

Surgical procedures are required in most recurrent dislocations of the shoulder. These surgical techniques involve some form of "tightening" of the joint structures. Operations performed to prevent recurrence are quite effective. Excellent results are seen in most cases. Prior to and following surgery, the physician may recommend therapeutic exercises for the muscles involved in the area. Exercise is almost always recommended following surgery for recurrent dislocations. The exercise routines recommended in Chapter 12 are designed for this purpose.

Strength-developing exercises, unfortunately, have little effect on restabilizing the acromio-clavicular and sterno-clavicular joints because the muscles in these areas do not actually cross these joints. Therefore, strengthening exercises do little for increasing joint stability—not that therapeutic exercise following inactivity which resulted from an injury to either of these two joints will not be beneficial. To the contrary, muscle strengthening in any area which has been inactive due to injury is worthwhile. But the benefits lie mostly in the rehabilitation of the individual with subsequent improvement of his performance. Muscular performance usually deteriorates as a result of muscular weakness.

THE ELBOW AND WRIST

Elbow

The elbow joint is normally quite stable. It allows a hinge action between the humerus and ulna. Furthermore, there is a rotation action between the humerus and the radius. Much force is required to dislocate this joint. Up to the point of dislocation, the injury is called a sprain. Sprains of the elbow are frequent. Although the elbow joint is stable, any slight amount of injury tends to result in discomfort and the inability to make effective use of the arm in general.

If the individual attempts to break a fall with an outstretched arm, the elbow sometimes becomes hyperextended. This hyperextension may result in sprains to the limiting ligaments, or, if enough pressure is applied, the joint may dislocate. An arm that is struck from the rear while the elbow is hyperextended is susceptible to being dislocated. The force tends to drive the joint forward. This action causes a dislocation. Chip fractures may be associated with this type of injury. These chips may become loose bodies within the joint.

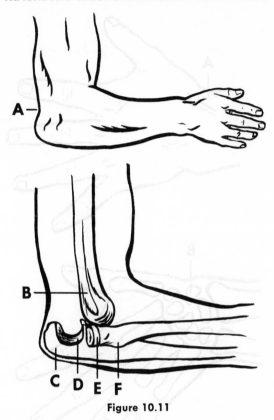

Figure 10.11

A dislocation of the elbow is shown in Figure 10.11. The ulna (C) is displaced posteriorly, resulting in an indentation in the back of the elbow, pointed out at A. The humerus (B) rides out of the olecranon fossa (D). The head of the radius (E) is also disarticulated from the humerus. The proximal end of the radius is noted at F.

Wrist

Mechanism of Injury. Wrist injuries are most often a result of hyperextension of the joint. Other than sprains, the most common injury to the wrist is a fracture of the navicular bone indicated at B in Figure 10.12. The wrist may dislocate, but such an injury is

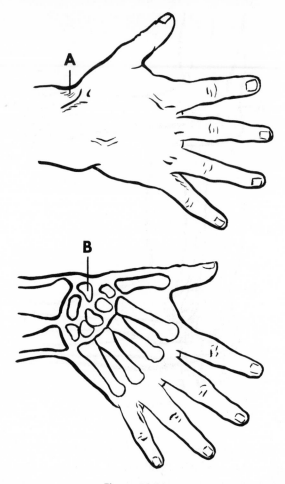

Figure 10.12

extremely rare. Long after a diagnosis of a "wrist sprain" in which there was persistent pain, it is often discovered that a fracture was the original problem. The damage resulting to the bone may necessitate surgical removal of the bone. The site of pain related to the navicular fracture is located at what is often called the anatomical "snuff box." This area between the extensor tendons of the thumb on the radial side of the wrist is indicated at A in Figure 10.12.

Some medical services have a standing order that all X rays of the wrist should be repeated in two weeks after the original X ray. This is done to ascertain whether or not fractures of this bone have actually occurred. Many times the fracture is not seen on the first X ray.

Implications for Programming. Exercises for improving the stability of the elbow joint are described in Chapter 12. Exercises for the wrist and forearm involve the use of progressive-resistance techniques in flexion and extension of the wrist joint. The forearms may be stabilized by placing them on the knees while the individual is in the sitting position. Flexion exercises should be done in a supinated position (palms up) and extension exercises in the pronated position (palms down).

Selected References

Helfrich, H., *Fractures and Dislocations*. London: New Sydenham Society, 1899.

Logan, Gene A., "Instructional Slides for Athletic Training and Rehabilitation." Springfield, Mo.: Box 3535 Glenstone Station.

——, and Roland F. Logan, *Techniques of Athletic Training*, 2nd ed. Los Angeles: Franklin-Adams Press, 1959.

Morehouse, Laurence E., and Philip J. Rasch, *Scientific Basis of Athletic Training*. Philadelphia: W. B. Saunders Co., 1958.

Moseley, H. F., "Disorders of the Knee," *Ciba Clinical Symposia*, V, No. 6 (November-December 1953), 171–201.

——, "Disorders of the Hip," *Ciba Clinical Symposia*, V, No. 2 (March-April 1953), 35–60.

——, "Disorders of the Shoulder," *Ciba Clinical Symposia*, XI, No. 3 (May-June-July 1959), 75–102.

——, "Traumatic Disorders of the Ankle and Foot," *Ciba Clinical Symposia*, VII, No. 6 (November-December 1955), 167–194.

Thorndike, Augustus, *Athletic Injuries*, 5th ed. Philadelphia: Lea & Febiger, 1962.

Wiles, Philip, *Essentials of Orthopaedics*, 3rd ed. London: J. & A. Churchill Ltd., 1959.

Williams, J. G. P., *Sports Medicine*. London: Edward Arnold (Publishers) Ltd., 1962.

11

PRINCIPLES OF EXERCISE

The value of exercise for therapeutic purposes has been known and utilized for thousands of years. Perhaps the first medical application of muscular activity in disease was described by Mercurialis in the sixteenth century.[1] This Italian physician classified gymnastics into two kinds, (1) *preventive,* or conservative, and (2) *therapeutic.* Preventive gymnastics were for the healthy and therapeutic gymnastics were for the sick. His book *The Art of Gymnastics* was a forerunner of much of the work of physicians in the following centuries.

Much of our present day emphasis and usage of exercise for therapeutic purposes has grown out of the knowledge gained from war. Early *ambulation* (getting patients up after surgery as early as possible) was rarely used prior to World War II. Because of the demand for increased manpower and in order to make the earliest possible return of the wounded to service, great emphasis was placed upon rapid return to activity. Recovery time was found to decrease following early ambulation.

Near the end of World War II, Thomas L. DeLorme,[2] an

[1] L. H. Joseph, "Medical Gymnastics in the Sixteenth and Seventeenth Centuries," *Ciba Symposia,* X, No. 5 (March-April 1949), 1041–1053.

[2] "Restoration of Muscle Power by Heavy-Resistance Exercises," *Journal of Bone and Joint Surgery,* XXVII-A (October 1945), 645–667.

amateur weight lifter before he entered the Army Medical Corps, introduced what he called *progressive-resistance exercise* (P.R.E.). His method, since modified, along with early ambulation brought about widespread acceptance of therapeutic exercise by the medical profession. It should be pointed out, however, that the principles of exercise had been used many years previous to this time by athletic trainers and coaches who, as a result of pressures to return athletes to the game, had actually been utilizing early ambulation and various forms of resistance exercises.

Muscular activity may be used for the prevention, rehabilitation, and prevention of recurrence of adaptations made to internal and external forces that have been imposed upon the body. When exercise is used for the purposes of rehabilitation, it is generally referred to as therapeutic exercise. It must be remembered that the only real difference between therapeutic exercise and exercise in general is that the former is being used as a form of therapy. Therapeutic exercise is used to improve or to prevent regression of some physical deviation or disability.

One of the major objectives in any physical education program should be to provide conditioning to aid the body in withstanding external forces which might be injurious to the muscles, bones, and joints of the body. Through conditioning programs of exercise, the body is better able to resist situations that are potentially hazardous. Great emphasis should be placed upon this phase of the program. Many factors are involved when the program of injury prevention is to be considered. When the neuromuscular mechanism is in a well-conditioned state, the individual is able to react faster to a potential injury situation. Although basic reaction time is not improved, the body is able to respond in a more skillful way to avoid hazards. The basic elements of a prevention program involve the development of strength, endurance, flexibility, and skill. These factors will be discussed in detail from the standpoint of the prevention and rehabilitation of injuries, divergencies, and other conditions that prevent the individual from functioning at his potential.

Exercise, and more specifically therapeutic exercise, may be used for both general and specific outcomes. General outcomes of exercise include raising the threshold of physiological responses. Such components as better oxygen delivery, lowered pulse rate, better cardiac output, more rapid recovery from exertion, and other changes result from exercise. These benefits accrue provided that sufficient stress is applied to increase the tolerance level of the individual. Also, such things as appetite, general endurance, and an overall sense of well-being are outcomes provided by exercise. The specific outcomes of therapeutic exercise are primarily concerned with strength, endurance, flexibility, relaxation, and neuromuscular skill (coordination).

Therapeutic exercise may be classified into four kinds, (1) *passive*, (2) *active-assistive*, (3) *active*, and (4) *resistive*. These categories indicate a progression from very mild to intense exercise. The practical application of exercise progression may involve one or more of these categories. Passive exercise involves having a body segment or limb moved through a specific range of motion by another person. As this form of exercise is being administered, the individual may or may not be volitionally making an effort to perform the movement. In most instances, however, he is attempting to move the part but is unable to initiate or to demonstrate overt movement. This kind of exercise is seldom used in the school program. In active-assistive exercise, the individual moves a body part through a range of motion as far as possible and is then assisted to complete the movement. This form of exercise is usually performed against gravity with the body part acting as resistance against which the muscles work. Active exercise involves moving a body part through a range of motion against gravity unassisted by another individual. Technically, this type of exercise is a form of resistive exercise. Resistive exercises are those in which external forces are used to provide additional loads to increase the resistance to the movement. Various kinds of external forces may be used to provide the resistance. These include weights (in the form of metal plates), springs, rubber bands, pulleys, and other equipment of this type. In the case of *isometric* strength-development programs where muscular force is applied against one part of the body by another part, the part opposing the effort is the resistance.

When the exercise is used for therapeutic purposes, certain factors must be taken into consideration. These are factors not ordinarily of concern in the exercise program of normal individuals. Such factors include pain, limited ranges of motion, and uncoordinated neuromuscular relationships. Quite often the intensity of the exercise dosage is regulated by the individual's ability to withstand pain upon movement. Since this pain is often heightened by the fear of pain, a two-fold problem exists for the therapist. Limited range of motion may result from a swelling or fluid within the joint. As a consequence, it is not necessarily related to shortened tendons and other structures in the area. Attention must be paid to this possible cause of the lack of normal movement. A careful consideration of the differences in the causes of decreased range of motion will provide a better foundation upon which to base the exercise program. The term uncoordinated as used here relates to the inability of muscles to function in a proper relationship to each other. A coordinated movement is one in which a smooth working together of bodily parts or individual muscles or muscle groups exists. Again, pain may be the cause for some of the uncoordinated movements. In some congenital or pathological conditions, the problem of uncoordinated movement is of major concern. Cerebral-palsy patients often manifest such movements.

The ability of the human body to make adaptations is of major concern when the applications of exercise are considered. Generally, the body is waging a constant battle against such external forces as gravity and other kinds of stresses. These may or may not result in certain adaptations which might be disadvantageous to the physical well-being of the individual. A reversal of these changes often can be made through exercise. Since the body has many mechanisms that provide it with the ability to adapt favorably in the direction desired by the individual, it can be said that exercise facilitates the performance of subsequent exercise. The obverse holds also, because inactivity results in lessening the ability to do exercise, and many of the undesirable adaptations which are seen in inactive people result. The use of exercise for ameliorating adaptive deviations that stem from the force of gravity, congenital anomalies, and traumatic disabilities is a major concern of this chapter.

When the individual performs exercise for either normal or therapeutic purposes, his body has the ability to respond to this exercise in specific ways. In order for favorable adaptations to occur, demands that are sufficient to increase the tolerance for more exercise must be placed upon the organism. Since the body has this ability for specific adaptations to the demands placed upon it, a unifying principle has been suggested to serve as a general guide for the development or design of an exercise program. This concept has been called the "SAID" principle.[3] The name is composed of the first letters of the following words: "Specific Adaptation to Imposed Demands." The "SAID" principle offers a guide to gain maximum effect in the least amount of time with a minimum amount of effort. Strength, endurance, flexibility, relaxation, and coordination may be developed by using this principle in the application of exercise.

General principles of applied exercise may provide ways by which the most rapid development may occur in the most efficient manner. In designing specific exercises based upon general principles of exercise, the three "I's" suggested by Dr. Eleanor Metheny of the University of Southern California are helpful. They stand for the three words "Identify, Isolate, and Intensify." These three procedures should be utilized in the order indicated when designing exercises or routines of exercises for an adapted physical education program.

As an example of the application of the three "I's," the *sit-up*, a strength-developing exercise for the abdominal muscles, will be used. First, one must *identify* the area to be exercised. In this case it is the abdominal muscles. In order to *isolate* as much as possible the muscles to be exercised, the body should be placed in a position which allows the most effective and efficient application of muscular force in the desired area. When isolating the area for exercise, attention must be given to the stabilization of other parts of the body. In stabilizing for adequate exertion in the abdominal area, the knees and hips are generally flexed with the individual lying on the back with the feet placed under some structure. This prevents the feet from coming up from the floor during the exercise. Finally, in order for progression to occur, the individual must *intensify* the exercise within his tolerance to perform the exercise.

Perhaps the mildest form of this exercise beyond merely tensing the muscles would be to lift the head from the floor. One *progression* in intensity would involve lifting the head. Another progression in intensity would involve lifting the shoulders and

[3] Earl L. Wallis and Gene A. Logan, *Figure Improvement and Body Conditioning through Exercise* (Englewood Cliffs, N.J.: Prentice-Hall, Inc., 1964), p. 1.

upper back from the floor while the arms are folded in front of the body. Next, the complete sit-up would be performed with the arms projecting forward along the sides of the knees. A further progression might be to perform a sit-up with the hands clasped together behind the neck. The elbows are held back as far as possible. For greater intensity, weight can be held behind the head during the exercise. The steps in designing any exercise involve identification, isolation, and intensification.

STRENGTH

The ability of the muscles to exert force, has been studied more than any other single element of human performance. The importance of adequate levels of strength are universally recognized. Although an adequate definition of strength is not available, much is known and can be said about this factor from a functional or operational standpoint. Strength undergirds all other factors when one considers the total functioning of the body in movement. Without sufficient strength, factors such as endurance, flexibility, and skill cannot be used effectively. Continued muscular activity must be performed in order to prevent a deterioration of these factors when inactivity occurs. When activity which is necessary for minimal functioning of the body is decreased, strength, along with other performance factors, tends to be lost. When the muscle and surrounding tissues begin to waste away as a result of inactivity, this depreciation of tissue is termed *atrophy*.

Strength-Development Principles

Strength development, which results in increased ability to exert force, increased bulk (hypertrophy), and increased tone or firmness of the muscular tissue, is an important beneficial aspect of therapeutic exercise. Although it is not scientifically proven as to which method or technique is the most efficient for developing strength, enough information is known to satisfactorily establish therapeutic exercise programs for the improvement of strength.

No matter what method or technique of strength development is utilized for therapeutic exercise, one basic principle must be kept in mind. That is the *overload principle*. The overload principle is the application of increasing demands or overload beyond those levels of activity previously attained. There must be an intensification of imposed demands to raise the tolerance level of the individual. Once the ability to exert force at a given level is attained, further increases in demands must be applied in order for additional increases to accrue.

Basically, two forms of strength conditioning are in general use. These involve exercising against resistance in such a way that the muscles either work, create muscular tension without changing their length, or do so while changing their length. Exercise in which exertion is offered without changing the length of the muscle or moving the part through a range of motion is known as *isometric* contraction. Exercise which employs changing the length of the muscle while the part is being moved through a range of motion is known as *isotonic* contraction. There are advantages and disadvantages in the use of these two types of exercise in terms of strength development.

In recent years, the isometric-contraction strength-development exercise has received much attention. Studies comparing isometric and isotonic strength-development exercises have shown very little difference in the development of strength *per se,* the ability to exert force. From the standpoint of time expended, isometric-contraction exercise is more efficient than isotonic exercise. Although isometric-contraction exercise is most efficient from the standpoint of time, it has limitations. Performing an isometric or no-movement type exercise places little stress on the circulatory and respiratory systems. Therefore, only small changes in circulatory-respiratory endurance are made. Also, desired bulk or hypertrophy does not increase at as rapid a rate in isometric-contraction exercise as it does in isotonic-contraction exercise.

In terms of therapeutic exercise, isometric contraction has some advantages, particularly where minimal joint motion is desired. Isotonic or movement exercise has greater therapeutic value where reduction of pain and an increase in a range of motion is desired. With isotonic exercise, the individual is able to see increases in his ability to overcome resistances. If resistances of known weights are used in the program, it is obvious to the person just how much improvement he has made from day to day. Thus, the factor of motivation may cause the individual to respond more rapidly if he uses isotonic-contraction exercises.

It is widely believed that for individuals requiring therapeutic exercise, isotonic programs are superior to isometric programs. Hellebrandt,[4] an outstanding authority in this field, has indicated that isotonic exercise is preferred to isometric exercise when strength is the desired outcome.

Strength-Development Procedures

There are two basic methods in use for the development of strength. The most widely accepted and recommended one is based upon the technique developed by DeLorme,[5] *progressive-resistance exercise*. It involves determining the resistance which can be lifted or overcome ten times, or ten *repetitions*. The performance of ten repetitions through a range of motion is called a *bout*. DeLorme and Watkins[6] recommended the use of either two bouts or three bouts per day per exercise. The first step in this method is the determination of the ten-repetition maximum (10 R.M.). The 10 R.M. is that resistance with which the individual may perform no more than ten movements through the range of motion. The resistance is determined through a process of trial and error. When three bouts are used, the first bout consists of one-half maximum resistance, the second bout involves three-fourths maximum resistance, and the third bout consists of maximum resistance (10 R.M.). The first two bouts in the series serve as a warm-up for the final maximum effort. A modification of this procedure and the one suggested for use in adapted physical education classes is the performance of two bouts per day per exercise. The first bout should consist of one-half maximum resistance performed ten repetitions. The second bout should consist of maximum resistance performed ten repetitions. Empirical observation of this procedure in adapted physical education has indicated that it is more applicable than the use of three bouts.

4 Frances A. Hellebrandt, "The Scientific Basis of Weight Training" in *Weight Training in Sports and Physical Education* (Washington: American Association for Health, Physical Education and Recreation, 1962), p. 27.

5 Thomas L. DeLorme and Arthur L. Watkins, *Progressive Resistance Exercise* (New York: Appleton-Century-Crofts, Inc., 1951).

6 *Ibid*.

The following example of the two-bout procedure will serve as an illustration. If the individual found that he could lift 20 pounds no more than ten repetitions during a trial and error initial session, in the succeeding exercise period he would begin by performing ten repetitions with 10 pounds of resistance. He would finish by doing ten repetitions with 20 pounds. As the ability to perform more than ten repetitions with the 20 pounds develops, more repetitions can be performed by the individual. When he can reach twelve to thirteen repetitions, the weight or resistance should be increased to cause him to return to approximately ten repetitions. In practical application, it is suggested that the repetitions remain between eight and twelve, because it is rather difficult to reach an exact number of ten repetitions at all times. The point to remember here is that the repetitions should remain fairly constant while the resistance is progressively increased in subsequent exercise periods. Throughout this book, where strength exercises are indicated, the foregoing procedures are recommended except where other specific instructions are made.

The second method of strength-development exercise involves exerting a *submaximal* or *maximal effort* for approximately six to ten seconds. This exercise involves no movement of the part during the exercise and is the basic procedure for isometric exercise. This specific procedure was introduced in this country by Hettinger and Müller of Germany.[7] However, before the introduction of the studies of these investigators in 1953, a similar form of isometric exercise called "dynamic tension" was promoted by Charles Atlas. The original recommendation made by Hettinger and Müller was to apply *two-thirds maximal* effort to a muscle group. This contraction was to be held for six seconds per day. It has been found more recently that applying *maximal* resistance up to ten seconds once or twice per day will yield greater results. It is recommended here that a maximal effort lasting for approximately ten seconds applied once per day is sufficient. In some instances, specific application of isometric exercise might provide more favorable results than isotonic exercises.

[7] Erich A. Müller, "The Regulation of Muscular Strength," *Journal of the Association for Physical and Mental Rehabilitation*, XI, No. 2 (March-April 1957), 41–47.

ENDURANCE

Endurance, the ability to sustain prolonged physical activity, is gained by regularly increasing effort and gradually progressing in *repetitions* and/or *rate* of activity. As a result, the individual's tolerance for more of the same type of activity will be increased. In other words, demands must be imposed which cause the body to make specific adaptations.

A close relationship exists between the factors of strength and endurance. As one of these factors is developed, the other also evidences an increase.[8] Strength is more prerequisite to endurance than vice versa. The development of strength must precede endurance training. Endurance development is at least a two-fold mechanism. First, there is a general overall elevation of the basic adaptations. Examples are (1) increased oxygen-carrying capacity of the blood, (2) the bringing into operation of more capillaries, and (3) greater cardiac output. Second, very specific endurances result in areas of the body when they are called upon to exert continued and prolonged effort. Therefore, various parts of the body may develop a greater endurance than other parts, provided that sufficient specific training is followed. Thus, it can be said that there is a general endurance that is basically circulatory-respiratory. In addition, there are specific endurances that result from specific training of a muscle or group of muscles for a given task. This division could be referred to as *circulatory-respiratory endurance* and *muscular endurance*. The relationship between these two types of endurance is not completely understood.

In terms of therapeutic exercise, endurance is usually considered a part of strength exercises for specialized areas or specific parts of the body. Usually, when general conditioning programs are desired, endurance becomes an important factor. In adapted physical education, endurance development is of major concern for those students who have conditions warranting the reduction of physical fatigue. Endurance helps to allay the discomforts of fatigue.

Perhaps the most effective program now in use for the develop-

8 Michael Yessis, "Relationships between Varying Combinations of Resistances and Repetitions in the Strength-Endurance Continuum" (Doctoral dissertation, University of Southern California, 1963).

ment of both strength and endurance at the same time is *circuit training.* This program was developed by Morgan and Adamson[9] of England. In the adapted physical education class where several students have common disabilities for which a general conditioning program is medically recommended and where little equipment is available, this procedure is invaluable. It should be emphasized that when utilizing this type of program in adapted physical education classes very careful attention must be given to the tolerance of the individual students. Circuit training should be limited to those individuals requiring a general-conditioning type of activity. The diagnosis and medical recommendation received from the physician must guide the application of such a program. Since circuit training involves the "station" approach with groups of students moving from one exercise or exercise area to another, administrative problems can be reduced. This procedure utilizes active and resistive exercises established on the basis of the abilities and tolerances of the participants. Primarily, a series of six to ten exercises comprises the ·circuit. Examples of the exercises, or stations, are (1) overhead ladder, (2) pull-up, (3) push-up, (4) biceps curl with weight, (5) half knee-bend with weight, (6) back-raise, (7) sit-up, or any similar kinds of activities. The amount of resistance for each of these activities depends upon the ability and tolerance of the individuals involved. Thus, the resistance or load for each activity is established in relation to the student with the lowest exercise tolerance. He must be able to perform at least ten repetitions of the exercise. For example, for the biceps curl exercise in a class, the weight to be lifted may be determined by trial and error to be 30 pounds. This weight is used by all individuals in the class.

With a set resistance established at each station, each individual on the first day performs as many repetitions as he can at each exercise station. The number of repetitions for each individual for each station is recorded. Prior to the next exercise period, the number of repetitions is arbitrarily reduced by one-third (or one-half, if desired). For example, if a student did fifteen repetitions, his repetitions would be reduced to ten. On succeeding days, the exercise would be performed for ten repetitions with 30 pounds of resistance during one trip around the circuit. Three circuits would be completed during a class period of approximately thirty minutes.

9 R. E. Morgan and G. T. Adamson, *Circuit Training* (New Rochelle, N.Y.: Sportshelf & Soccer Associates, 1958).

In other words, thirty repetitions of the biceps curl exercise would be performed with the 30-pound weight.

A suggested program might include seven exercises to be completed in thirty minutes by twenty-one students. Administratively, the class might be divided into seven groups of three. These groups would continue as units in order to assist each other in maintaining proper exercise positioning. They would also stand ready to receive the weight as a safety precaution. Furthermore, this procedure would facilitate a continuous movement around the circuit. As the performance of the exercises becomes easier, the number of repetitions at each station can be increased by two. Thus, a student who was originally performing ten repetitions would perform two more repetitions of the exercise on each of the three circuits. Where weights are used at stations, the weight might be increased 5 to 10 pounds depending upon the group's tolerance. These changes are uniformly made at intervals of two to three weeks.

When exercise is used for therapeutic reasons, the development of endurance usually involves a specific part of the body. Therefore, if more endurance is desired than that which is obtained through a regimen of strength-development exercises previously discussed, the rate and number of repetitions should be increased while using a light resistance. As the individual is able to increase the rate and number of repetitions of the exercise over the previous levels, the amount of resistance should be gradually increased. The exercise must be such that it involves the circulatory-respiratory mechanism to a greater degree than does strength-development exercise. For example, an exercise used for strength development may involve 10 pounds of resistance for ten repetitions. The same exercise, when used for the development of endurance, might be performed with 5 pounds of resistance for twenty or more repetitions at a more rapid rate. Therefore, the resistance rate and number of repetitions to be used depend upon the desired outcomes of the exercise.

FLEXIBILITY

Flexibility, the range of motion of joints or parts of the body, is an important aspect for consideration in terms of therapeutic exercise. It is possible that a person may have too much as well as not enough flexibility, but the latter is usually the case. Most limitations in flexibility result from adaptive shortening of the connective tissues that cross and surround joints. Undesired extremes of flexibility due to injury or congenital pathological involvement of these same structures may result in their being elongated. Their condition would allow the joints or body parts more range of motion than may be desired for proper functioning. Many of these *hyperflexible* areas may not return to a desired state of flexibility without surgical intervention. However, therapeutic exercise is extremely beneficial in strengthening the muscles whose major function is to stabilize these joints. Strengthening the muscles in areas where the connective tissues, ligaments and other joint structures, allow more range of motion than is desired will tend to provide better functioning through the resultant increased joint stability.

The term "flexibility," as commonly used in physical education, has connotations implying only flexion of joints or body parts. As employed here, the term indicates the total range of movement that is possible at a joint.

Generally, the problem of decreased or limited flexibility is of greatest concern to most people. The pull of gravity on the erect biped stance of the human organism is largely responsible for decreased flexibility. This is very common where certain muscle weaknesses exist. As pointed out previously, man is in constant search for extension of the body. In his attempt to maintain himself in an upright stance, gravity is constantly pulling downward. Where inactivity, no matter what the cause, prevents optimum strength, flexibility often becomes a problem. For example, if the abdominal muscles are weak, there is a tendency for the pelvis to tilt forward (iliac crest) with a resultant increased low-back or lumbar curvature. If this increased lumbar curvature is maintained for long periods, the fascial structures and other connective tissue in the lumbar area will adapt to this habitual postural position by shortening, which is often accompanied by short hamstring and rectus femoris muscles. Once this adaptation has occurred, the range of motion in the area is limited to such an extent that no matter how strongly the abdominal muscles are developed, their ability to shorten to their potential is seriously curtailed. It follows that in order to bring about proper alignment of the pelvis, the shortened connective tissue in the lumbar area will have to be increased in length. This relationship of adaptively shortened structures on one side of the body and weakened muscles on the other side calls for a reversal of these conditions for optimum function. This reversal involves increasing the flexibility in the lumbar area by stretching (lengthening) the posterior structures and strengthening the abdominal muscles.

The situation where there is shortened connective tissue on one side of the joint or body part and weakened muscles on the other side might be likened to the bow used by archers. The bow string in this analogy would represent the adaptively shortened structures. Throughout this book, a concept which shall be referred to as the *lengthening-strengthening principle* will be applied where such a relationship exists: one should *stretch* the shortened structures and *strengthen* the opposite weakened muscles. It must be emphasized that muscles with *optimum amplitude,* those that are being "stretched," may also be strong muscles. Decreased flexibility resulting from adaptations to habitual positioning involves connective tissue which is *noncontractile.* The muscle fibers, which contract and relax and thereby cause the muscle to change its length, are surrounded by connective tissue. This connective tissue holds bundles of the fibers together, envelops total muscles, and forms tendons and ligaments. So, in effect, what is being stretched or increased by flexibility exercises is the noncontractile connective tissue. Therefore, the strengthening exercises involve increasing the ability of the muscle fibers to exert force. This product is largely separate from changes made in the connective tissue.

The increase of flexibility involves a long process. Flexibility is gained by the application of increased effort at regular intervals. At the same time, there is a gradually increased demand for range of motion. In the administration of any general exercise program, flexibility exercises should follow endurance exercises but precede strength exercises. Where specific problems exist, particularly in terms of therapeutic exercise, endurance exercise that stimulates the circulatory-respiratory system tends to aid the flexibility procedures. This is probably a result of an increase in temperature within the connective tissue itself. The exercise bout must be very long for this process to occur. Other factors also play a part. The effect of temperature increase is not clearly understood. The whole general area of "warm-up," whether for normal or therapeutic purposes, requires further study.

Since muscles on opposite sides of joints work *reciprocally* with each other, there must be relaxation of one muscle while the other muscle is contracting. To stretch the adaptively shortened fascia and other connective tissue in an area, the muscles must relax to allow elongation of these structures to occur. If relaxation were not able to take place, the muscles would tend to resist the stretching action. When an area in which muscle is also located is being stretched, the muscle resists the stretch. When the muscles opposite those being stretched are contracted, the muscles of the involved area are *reflexly inhibited.* This reflex inhibition allows for a more favorable setting in which increased range of motion may occur. Stretching activates a built-in protective mechanism, the muscular proprioceptors, which brings about reflex contraction of muscle tissue. This is evident when rapid forceful movements are made. In order to minimize this reflex contraction it is recommended that stretching be controlled and done slowly without momentum of body parts.

Slow stretching procedures advocated by Robert E. Shelton, University of Illinois, have been shown to be successful by means of observation and investigation. One study[10] of the effect of slow and fast stretching on the sacro-femoral angle indicated that although a slow-stretching group and a fast-stretching group made about equal gains in range of motion, the fast-stretch group noted pain and discomfort in the areas being stretched.

It has been hypothesized, as a result of empirical observation made on large numbers of athletes and the results of this and other related studies, that fast, uncontrolled stretching prior to an athletic event may be a predisposing cause for subsequent soft-tissue damage. This damage is often in the form of pulled muscles, particularly when maximum exertions are made. It appears plausible that slow, controlled stretching is an important preventive factor in terms of muscle tears. Although the individual who is performing therapeutic exercises is not generally required to exert maximal effort immediately after the stretching or flexibility exercises, it would

---

[10] Gene A. Logan and Glen H. Egstrom, "The Effects of Slow and Fast Stretching on the Sacro-Femoral Angle," *Journal of the Association for Physical and Mental Rehabilitation,* XV, No. 3 (May-June 1961), 85–89.

seem that slow, controlled stretching would allow for further range of motion. Pain or irritation is not usually experienced with this procedure.

Lack of flexibility generally results from inactivity that allows adaptive shortening to take place in connective tissue. Individuals requiring flexibility exercises in the adapted physical education class are often placed there immediately after the removal of casts. Immobilized joints soon lose flexibility. Pain and swelling usually accompany these cases. There is often apprehension on the part of the individual. There is a tendency for the person to resist movement of the part because of anticipation of possible pain during movement. Caution must always be taken when these exercises are performed. However, in order for increases in range of motion to occur, the part must be carried to the point of pain and slightly beyond. In the adapted physical education class, flexibility exercises are usually performed actively by the individual himself. He should be instructed in what to expect and how far the part should be carried through a given range of movement. Flexibility exercises performed in the class are limited to those that the individual can perform under his own volition.

RELAXATION

The ability to relax under the "tensions" and "stresses" of contemporary living is becoming an ever increasing problem. An understanding of the purpose and of the value of relaxation techniques—particularly in the adapted physical education program—is of great importance. Relaxation can be approached from at least two viewpoints. These are (1) *natural* relaxation and (2) *conscious* relaxation. In either case, the major purpose is for the provision of emotional release from "tensions." The ability to relax at will appears to be an important tool for the release of "tension."

The first approach to relaxation is natural relaxation. This form of relaxation comes as a result of the individual having participated in physical activity in the form of sports, games, and other physical activities. There is an awareness of an exhilarating feeling, which provides for emotional release from "stresses." If the activity in which the individual participates is pleasant and satisfying, the subsequent result is general relaxation.

The second approach to relaxation is concerned with offering the individual techniques through which he may become consciously aware of muscular tension. As a result, he will be able to release that tension. Several methods have been advocated. Perhaps the most widely utilized is that developed by Jacobson.[11] This technique is called *progressive relaxation*. This technique involves a person's learning to recognize the "feeling" of muscular tension in a muscle or group of muscles. After the awareness of the feeling of muscular tension is perceived, several procedures are used to help release that tension. The release of tension (relaxation) is usually begun in a specific muscle or group of muscles and practiced until it becomes learned. The procedure is then practiced in other areas until relaxation is gained throughout the body. The ability to relax volitionally is acquired in about the same manner as any other neuromuscular skill is learned. The "feeling" of relaxation must be perceived in order for it to become a learned skill which can be reproduced when desired. This form of relaxation involves the conscious awareness of the individual and requires continued practice and application for optimum outcomes.

Many techniques for the promotion of relaxation are in current practice. Since the teaching-learning process is rather involved when applied in a therapeutic exercise program, the reader should consult the Appendix for basic books on the subject.

SKILL (NEUROMUSCULAR COORDINATION)

Skill, or neuromuscular coordination, is a factor for consideration in the therapeutic exercise program. A general misconception has produced a part of the literature for many years regarding the development of *general* coordination of the body. In using the term "coordination" to mean the ability to perform skilled acts, it is

[11] Edmund Jacobson, *Progressive Relaxation* (Chicago: University of Chicago Press, 1938).

generally accepted today that so-called "coordination exercises" will not bring about an improvement in overall motor performance. The development of skill, or neuromuscular coordination, requires instead a *specific* kind of approach. It might be said, nevertheless, that there are many coordinations or patterns of movement within the body. If these patterns are developed to a high degree, the end result could be called *general* coordination.

Exercises that develop strength, endurance, and flexibility provide a base upon which specific coordinations can be developed. The development of these factors does not necessarily bring about better total coordination. They do, however, contribute a foundation upon which skill can be developed. If a person desires to develop a particular pattern of movement, he must practice and learn that movement pattern in the way in which the subsequent performance is to be demonstrated.

In terms of therapeutic exercise, activities often termed "coordination exercises" are used to improve working interrelationships between and among muscles and muscle groups. Quite specific patterns of movement must be practiced to accomplish these relationships. Coordination in this sense means an ability of parts to work together in a smooth-functioning unity. For example, if one part of a muscle is weakened through disease, the pattern of movement of the lever upon which this muscle acts may not be that which is desired because only a part of the muscle was doing its share of the movement. The individual must either strengthen this part of the muscle to where it was before the disease, or he must learn to use it in such a way as to demonstrate a smooth, efficient movement pattern. This requires a very specific kind of training. The use of exercises to provide this kind of coordination has a very definite place in the therapeutic exercise program.

The exercises recommended throughout this book for the development of strength of different areas of the body may serve as coordination exercises of the type described previously. Exercises for this purpose are required at times in the early rehabilitation of injuries and debilitating diseases. In instances where exercise is to be administered for certain neurological conditions, cerebral palsy for example, specific recommendations would be made. Again, it must be stated that these exercises should be performed within the specific medical recommendation of the physician.

Selected References

Clarke, H. Harrison, and David H. Clarke, *Developmental and Adapted Physical Education*. Englewood Cliffs, N.J.: Prentice-Hall, Inc., 1963.

Davis, Elwood C., and Gene A. Logan, *Biophysical Values of Muscular Activity*. Dubuque, Iowa: Wm. C. Brown Co., 1961.

DeLorme, Thomas L., and Arthur L. Watkins, *Progressive Resistance Exercise*. New York: Appleton-Century-Crofts, Inc., 1951.

Kraus, Hans, *Therapeutic Exercise*. Springfield, Ill.: Charles C Thomas, 1949.

Kraus, Hans, and Wilhelm Raab, *Hypokinetic Disease*. Springfield, Ill.: Charles C Thomas, 1961.

Licht, Sidney, ed., *Therapeutic Exercise*. New Haven, Conn.: Elizabeth Licht, 1958.

Mathews, Donald K., et al., *The Science of Physical Education for Handicapped Children*. New York: Harper & Row, Publishers, 1962.

Metheny, Eleanor, *Body Dynamics*. New York: McGraw-Hill Book Co., Inc., 1952.

Morgan, R. E., and G. T. Adamson, *Circuit Training*. New Rochelle, N.Y.: Sportshelf & Soccer Associates, 1958.

Rathbone, Josephine L., *Corrective Physical Education*, 6th ed. Philadelphia: W. B. Saunders Co., 1959.

Sills, Frank D., ed., *Weight Training in Sports and Physical Education*. Washington, D.C.: American Association for Health, Physical Education and Recreation, 1962.

Wallis, Earl L., and Gene A. Logan, *Figure Improvement and Body Conditioning through Exercise*. Englewood Cliffs, N.J.: Prentice-Hall, Inc., 1964.

12

EXERCISE ROUTINES FOR COMMON CONDITIONS

EXERCISE-ROUTINE METHOD OF PROGRAMMING

Adapted physical education is basically an individual program. Since the student is assigned to the class on the basis of medical diagnosis and the recommendation of a physician, it is obvious that the classes will be composed of students with various physical disabilities.

The working relationship that is developed between the physical education department and the school health service is important. If this is a good relationship, the students who need adapted physical education will not be excused from physical education. The development of this relationship is discussed in detail in Chapter 14.

Because of the special nature of the students who compose the adapted physical education class, the teacher must have a functional relationship with the *individual* students who are in the *class*. Therefore, the classes must be smaller than those in the regular physical education program. A class of twenty students is considered ideal for optimum benefits.

Although a great variety of physical disabilities will be seen in adapted physical education classes, the individuals will generally fall into subgroups on the basis of similar disabilities. For example, in a class of twenty there might be five students rehabilitating knee disabilities; three might be taking exercises for common disabilities of the back; five might be recommended for postural exercises; the remainder might be recommended for a general conditioning program. It should be noted that the individuals in this class have disabilities requiring therapeutic exercise. Another class might consist of five students who were recommended for rehabilitation of joint disabilities. These students would be participating in therapeutic exercise, and the remaining fifteen students might be recommended for the sports phase of the program. Still another class could be composed exclusively of students requiring postural exercises. The composition of the class will depend upon the physical disabilities of the students who are unable to participate in the regular physical education program. Therefore, cooperation between the school health service and the physical education department is important.

The adapted physical education classes, because of the teacher-student relationship, present a greater administrative problem than do regular physical education classes. It is impossible to anticipate the kinds of medical classifications and recommendations that will be presented by the students entering the class for the first time. Since participation in the activity phase of the class should begin as soon as possible, it becomes the job of the instructor to streamline class administrative procedures. Therefore a guidebook or student handbook in which important underlying principles and pertinent information concerning the adapted physical education program are presented should be made available to the student. Such a handbook could serve at least three purposes: (1) it could facilitate the administration of the class; (2) it could provide a useful guide to the student while he is in the class; (3) it could be of some value for those individuals requiring a continued exercise program. The handbook might contain an introduction defining adapted physical education, the objectives of the program, indications of specific requirements for a given class, expected outcomes of therapeutic exercise, anatomical and physiological bases of exercise for specific conditions, and exercise routines for common disabilities found in the adapted physical education class. It might also contain information about the sports phase of the program and suggested recreational activities for individuals with certain physical limitations. Space should be provided for the student to record his program and progress by semesters. Handbooks have been developed for use in a number of programs.[1]

As a result of the frequency and similarity of certain disabilities, therapeutic exercise routines may be developed. The routine should include all of the exercises usually recommended for a common disability, thereby serving to provide a more efficient and comprehensive approach to the program. Furthermore, when the student appears the first time in an adapted physical education class, it will be possible to schedule his routine of exercises at that time on the basis of his classification and medical recommendation. Although it may be necessary to modify the exercise routine for specific cases, the recommendations for exercise are similar in most common disabilities.

The *exercise-routine method* of administering therapeutic exercise has been developed to a high degree of utility by Robert E. Shelton of the University of Illinois. He was responsible for the design of many of the exercise routines presented in this chapter.[2] The back routine named for him is in widespread use. Many of these exercise routines, especially those presented for traumatic conditions, have been illustrated in previous publications.[3,4] However, this is the first time in which a complete description of each exercise has been given.

EXERCISE FOR DISABILITIES DUE TO GRAVITY

Development and maintenance of optimum levels of strength, endurance, flexibility, and skill (desired habitual patterns of move-

[1] Gene A. Logan et al., *Student Handbook for Adapted Physical Education* (Dubuque, Iowa: Wm. C. Brown Co., 1960).

[2] Robert E. Shelton and Gene A. Logan, "Internal Derangements of the Knee and Common Back Disabilities" (paper presented to the Midwest Convention, American Association for Health, Physical Education and Recreation, Cincinnati, Ohio, 1952).

[3] *Ibid.*

[4] Gene A. Logan, "Instructional Slides for Athletic Training and Rehabilitation" (Springfield, Mo.: Box 3535 Glenstone Station).

ment) of the extensor mechanism of the body to withstand the constant pull of gravity is the key to providing a basis for "good" posture. Therefore, postural exercises should serve to (1) increase strength in specific areas for more efficient action; (2) increase muscular endurance to reduce the effects of fatigue and increase "staying power"; (3) increase flexibility in areas where connective tissues such as tendons, ligaments, and fascia have become adaptively shortened due to lack of mobility; and (4) improve skill in assuming desired segmental body alignments in many postures.

As pointed out previously, "good" posture is often considered synonymous with how well an individual is able to align himself with a plumb line in accordance with rigid standards that have a questionable origin. Teaching a person to assume this *static* position has some merit in making him aware of functional body alignment. But the use of such a position as an indication of the *functional* capacity of one's body is seriously limited. An individual never assumes this stiff, rigid standing position unless it is precisely to demonstrate his ability to align himself with the plumb line. Rather, observing the individual from a lateral or anterior-posterior view while the person is standing at ease *does* have merit, particularly when the concern is with the balance of segments. Alignment of the body so that it can be held in balance with a minimum of ligamentous, fascial, and muscular strain seems more desirable than a demonstration of the ability to assume a rigid position. To counteract disabilities due to gravity, the exercises are designed for the improvement of those physical fitness factors which serve to maintain balanced alignment.

The factors of strength, endurance, flexibility, and skill may be developed in a given individual. Without proper instruction in how desired balance of segments is to be maintained, little change may occur in that direction. Some evidence is available to indicate that a positive relationship exists between trunk strength and what is generally considered "good" posture.[5] This evidence suggests that strengthening the trunk might possibly result in better posture without attention to psychological awareness. When proper em-

5 M. Marilyn Flint and Bobbie Diehl, "Influence of Abdominal Strength, Back Extensor Strength and Trunk Strength Balance upon Antero-Posterior Alignment of Elementary School Girls," *Research Quarterly*, XXXII, No. 4 (December 1961), 490–498.

phasis is placed upon both psychological awareness and an effective exercise program, it should follow that better results could be obtained from a postural training program.

The intent here is to establish certain underlying principles as guidelines for the development of exercises. Examples of exercises are given to illustrate these principles. In some cases, the exercise routines may be complete for a specific area of the body and for a given condition. In terms of exercises which can be used to counteract gravitational-pull adaptations, the lengthening-strengthening principle is one of the basic concepts of exercise useful in postural training. This principle simply suggests that areas requiring increased flexibility should be stretched. The limiting connective tissues should be lengthened. The muscles in areas opposite or antagonistic to these structures should be strengthened through resistive exercises. Provided adequate attention is paid to psychological awareness of good body alignment, proper application of this principle will result in improvement of the desired factors discussed previously.

The exercise routines presented in the ensuing paragraphs are related to the conditions which were discussed in Chapter 8.

Antigravity Exercises for the Feet

Exercises for the feet involve an application of the *lengthening-strengthening principle*. This principle is applied to gain increased extensibility of connective tissue and strength of the supportive muscles in the medial longitudinal arch. Further reference should be made at this point to the kinesioanatomical relationships dealing with these structures illustrated in Chapter 6. Both *intrinsic* muscles (muscles that have both proximal and distal attachments in the same part—the foot in this case) and *extrinsic* muscles (muscles that have an attachment in one part and the other attachment in another part—the foot and leg) are involved in supporting the longitudinal arch. When a functional flat foot (eversion and abduction of the foot) is maintained for a long period, fibers on the lateral border of the Achilles tendon tend to become shorter. Those on the medial border become lengthened or, at least, they are not the same length as those on the lateral border. It is neces-

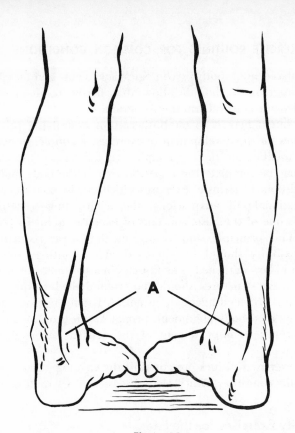

Figure 12.1

sary to reverse this relationship in order that a normal relationship can be reestablished.

An exercise for stretching the Achilles tendon is shown in Figure 12.1. It should be noted that the medial border of the tendon is placed in a shortened position as indicated at A. The heels should be placed approximately 8 to 10 inches apart. The great toes on each foot should be held closely together while the intrinsic muscles in the sole of the foot are strongly contracted to prevent stretching of the connective tissues in the sole of the foot. The soles of the feet should face each other (supination) to prevent rotating the calcaneus forward in a way that stretches the longitudinal arch. An attempt is also made to increase the extensibility of the Achilles tendon. The individual should stand approximately 3 feet from a wall in a "toe-in" position with the toes flexed strongly and the hands on the wall. The trunk should be allowed to move forward very slowly while the anterior muscles of the lower limbs

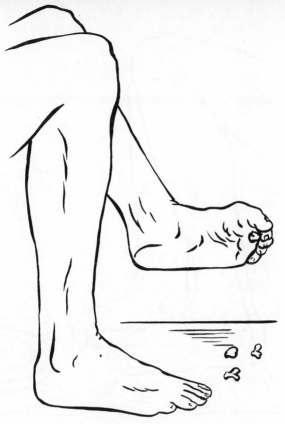

Figure 12.2

are strongly contracting. At the same time, the knees and hips should be held straight. The heels should remain in contact with the floor throughout the exercise. The movement should go to the point of pain and slightly beyond. This exercise should be repeated five to ten times. Care should be taken to avoid jerking movements.

A number of exercises may be utilized for strengthening the muscles that maintain the major arches of the foot. The illustrated exercises are used for this purpose. The important factor to remember is that the exercise should result in a reversal of eversion and abduction (pronation) of the foot. The sitting position is recommended for this exercise because it places the foot in a functional position but does not require total weight bearing during the exercise. An exercise is shown in Figure 12.2 for strengthening the arch by gripping with the toes. In order to help the individual sense the feeling of toe-gripping, small wads of paper may be placed

Figure 12.3

on the floor in a position that can be reached easily. These pieces of paper should be picked up by forcefully gripping with the toes. The student should place the papers in the hand opposite the foot being exercised. This procedure should be repeated five to ten times during each exercise period with both feet. In acute arch difficulty, the procedure may be used to advantage two or three times a day.

Another foot-strengthening exercise is shown in Figure 12.3. This exercise makes it possible to increase the resistance progressively to the intrinsic muscles of the foot by placing increased loads on a bath towel. The towel should be stretched to its full length. The weight is placed at one end of the towel and the feet rest on the opposite end. The object is to grip with the toes of each foot alternately. If done properly, the weight will be pulled toward the feet. This procedure should be repeated from ten to fifteen times.

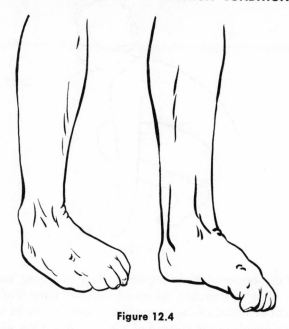

Figure 12.4

An exercise which is performed in the standing position is shown in Figure 12.4. This strengthening exercise should not be used until the individual has an awareness of forcefully contracting the intrinsic muscles of the foot. The toes should be curled inward while the feet are held in a position of inversion. The individual should walk on the sides of the feet and take short steps. The exercise position should be held while the person walks until a state of mild fatigue is experienced. As the tolerance of the individual increases, the distance of the walk should be increased.

Antigravity Flexibility Exercises

Gravitational pull on the upright body when insufficient muscle tone and endurance are present often produces increased curvatures of the spine and a forward hanging of the shoulders. If these postural deviations are maintained habitually for long periods of time, adaptive shortening of the connective tissues may prevent

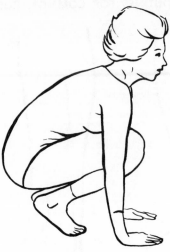

Figure 12.5

normal functioning of body segments. The shortened connective structures must be stretched. Increased mobility must result before realignment or repositioning of the body segments can be achieved. Increased strength in the absence of adequate flexibility solves only part of the postural deviation.

The most frequently observed sites of connective-tissue adaptation are in the posterior cervical and lumbar regions, anterior shoulder-girdle area, and hip joint. The antigravity flexibility exercises which follow are designed to increase mobility in these areas. A number of flexibility exercises may also be applicable for promoting mobility. Those included here are specific to the area indicated. If executed properly, these exercises will provide optimum results.

A flexibility exercise for the lumbar spine and the structures involved at the posterior aspect of the hip joint is shown in Figure 12.5. Starting from the position indicated, the individual should attempt to straighten the knees as far as possible while the hands remain in contact with the floor. The exercise should be repeated five to ten times.

An exercise to increase the flexibility of the spine is shown in Figure 12.6. Both the starting position and the execution of the exercise are shown. The pull of the hands adds the force necessary to bring about trunk rotation. This movement should be repeated five to ten times to each side. A special effort should be made to

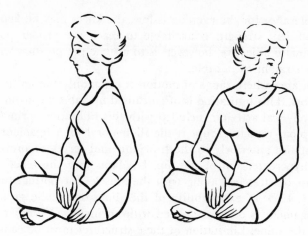

Figure 12.6

rotate the head during the stretch in order to increase mobility in the cervical area.

Figure 12.7

A flexibility exercise for the upper-back and neck regions is illustrated in Figure 12.7. The exercise should be started from a supine position. The upper limbs are away from the sides of the body at a 45-degree angle. By pushing downward with the hands, assistance is given in raising the lower limbs over the head to the position shown. This movement should be repeated five to ten times. If difficulty is encountered in getting the legs over the head when tolerance for the exercise is low, the knees may be kept bent until sufficient strength is available to reach the proper position. The ultimate objective, however, is to assume the position with the knees as straight as possible.

An area where range of motion is commonly limited is in the hip flexors. This limitation is often caused by habitual sitting and a lack of physical activity. Included with this limitation, primarily of the iliopsoas muscle group, is the iliofemoral or Y-ligament. This ligament lies anteriorly to the hip joint and serves to prevent excessive hyperextension of the hip. It adapts to a shortened length and must be stretched along with the muscles for normal function to occur. Lack of extensibility of the iliopsoas muscle group and the Y-ligament is often associated with an increased lumbar curvature of the spine. Limitation of these structures must be considered in exercise programs designed for the correction of postural faults.

Figure 12.8

A flexibility exercise for the flexors and the Y-ligament of the left hip is shown in Figure 12.8. With the individual in the position shown, the pelvis should be forced forward with pressure on the left hip. Caution must be used to ensure that the *abdominals are con-*

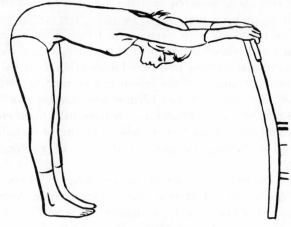

Figure 12.9

tracted. This safeguard is necessary to prevent an excessively increased curvature in the lumbar spine. The exercise should be repeated to both sides from five to ten times.

A flexibility exercise for the adductors of the shoulder girdle is illustrated in Figure 12.9. Standing in the position indicated, the individual should attempt to lower the head and trunk while holding the upper limbs as straight as possible. Maintaining the knees in an extended position also facilitates stretching the posterior hip and thigh muscles. The exercise should be repeated from five to ten times. Jerking movements should be avoided.

Antigravity Isometric Exercises

Maintenance of a desirable erect posture against the constant pull of gravity requires strength, endurance, and flexibility. In addition, attention must be directed toward the improvement of skill in assuming segmental body alignment. In order that the individual may volitionally assume an aesthetically pleasing posture, particularly in standing, he must become kinesthetically aware of the feeling of the desired position. The use of isometric or statically held strength-development exercises is helpful in heightening the awareness of good segmental alignment. From the standpoint of postural awareness, isometric exercises are most helpful in learning or acquiring postural perception. Isotonic exercises, however, tend to be superior to isometric exercises in terms of improved circulatory fitness and related factors such as hypertrophy and mobility.

Traditional starting positions for exercises used by most advocates of static posture development can be used as starting positions for isometric exercises. Numerous starting positions for exercises may be devised. However, only those basic to the erect standing position are described. The major purpose of including them is for use in helping the individual learn to assume an erect position.

The exercises described in the following series are based on some of the traditional starting positions for exercise. Assuming the position and holding it for approximately ten seconds with maximal contraction of one or more of the major antigravity muscles is an exercise in and of itself. Attention must be focused upon the desired body alignment while the exercise is being performed.

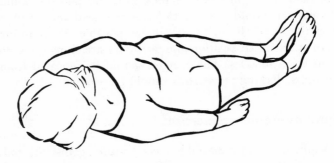

Figure 12.10

A supine position with the upper limbs along the sides is shown in Figure 12.10. The lumbar and cervical regions of the spine should be flattened as nearly as possible. To perform a postural exercise from this position, the individual should tighten the abdominal and gluteal muscles. At the same time, he should press down with the back of the head, the hands, and the heels. Maximum contraction should be held about ten seconds. The exercise may be repeated once or twice to heighten postural awareness. Furthermore, the exercise may also provide an opportunity for sufficient strength increases.

A variation of this back-lying exercise for the improvement of the positioning of the scapulae can be achieved by changing the position of the upper limbs. In the back-lying position with the upper limbs at a 90-degree angle to the body, the hands should be placed palm downward for the application of pressure. The exercise is performed by forcing downward with the hands. This action exerts a maximum contraction in the posterior shoulder muscles and scapular adductor muscles. In this same position with the upper arm at a 90-degree angle to the body, the elbows may be flexed to 90 degrees, with the forearms perpendicular to the floor. Pressure is exerted downward with the back of the upper arm and elbow. It may be necessary for the knees to be slightly flexed during the attempt to align the body while forcing downward on the lumbar area of the spinal column.

Figure 12.11

A hook-lying position is illustrated in Figure 12.11. The knees and hips should be flexed with the feet and legs parallel. A postural exercise from this position involves maximal contraction of the abdominal and gluteal muscles. The contraction is held for ten seconds. The exercise should be repeated once or twice during the exercise period. The position of the upper limbs may be changed to that suggested for the exercise illustrated in Figure 12.10.

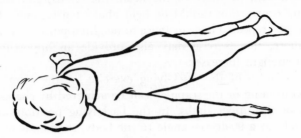

Figure 12.12

The front-lying or prone position is shown in Figure 12.12. The position of the head is either (1) with the forehead contacting a mat or (2) with the face turned to one side. To perform a posture exercise from this position, the upper limbs may be at the sides or in other positions depending upon the comfort of the individual. The postural exercise consists of maximally contracting the abdominal and gluteal muscles. The contraction is held for ten seconds. This procedure may be repeated once or twice during the exercise session. Attention should be paid to fixing the pelvis so that the lumbar curvature is not excessively increased.

A cross-sitting or "tailor's sit" position is shown in Figure 12.13. The knees should be bent. The legs are crossed with the feet pulled in as close to the buttocks as possible. The individual should attempt to assume an erect position with the hands and upper limbs placed in a supporting position. The hand and arm positions may be varied either by placing the arms alongside the body or the hands in contact with the shin for the maintenance of the erect position. The postural exercise in the cross-sitting position involves maximally contracting the abdominal and gluteal muscles for approximately ten seconds. This exercise should be repeated once or twice. In this position, it is also possible to stretch the adductor muscles of the thighs by pressing downward on the knees with the hands. The position of the feet should be changed frequently to avoid discomfort on the lateral sides of the feet and ankles.

The erect standing position is illustrated in Figure 12.14. The body segments should be aligned in such a way that one segment falls directly over another. The feet should be parallel to each other

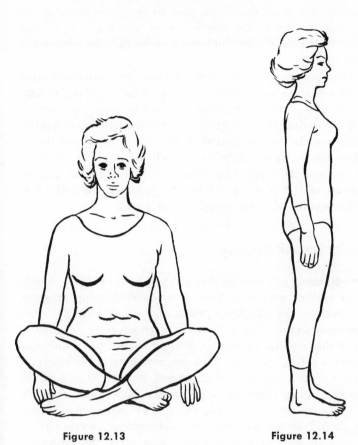

Figure 12.13   Figure 12.14

at approximately shoulder width. The knees should be flexed slightly. The pelvic position should be in a midposition between the extremes of anterior-posterior range of movement. In this position, the abdominal and the gluteal muscles are in a state of contraction. The amount of contraction should be sufficient to hold the pelvis in proper alignment. The chest should be lifted slightly. The head is held erect, but not forced uncomfortably backward. The shoulders should be level and relaxed. Standing in this position while maximally contracting the abdominal and gluteal muscles for approximately ten seconds is an effective postural exercise. This exercise should be repeated to heighten awareness of this position. Attention should be paid to the assumption of this erect standing position by the observation of oneself in a full-length mirror. Another person also could check to see that the correct posture is assumed.

A variation of the exercise is to have the individual stand with his back to the wall with his heels approximately 6 inches from the wall. In this position, an attempt would be made to force the lumbar spine against the wall at the same time that the abdominal and gluteal muscles are contracted. It may be necessary for the individual to flex the knees slightly to permit the pelvis to tilt to the desired position. Although this allowance is helpful in gaining an awareness of the pelvic position, the final goal should be to assume the position without support from a wall.

Antigravity Isotonic Exercises

Strengthening the muscles that serve to hold the body upright against the pull of gravity is basic to any conditioning program. Isometric exercises for the development of strength were described in the previous section. These isometric exercises were designed in such a way that emphasis could be directed toward the assumption of the erect standing posture. This form of exercise is especially helpful for the development of awareness of desirable erect positioning. However, since function is of greater importance than the ability to assume static positions, the use of antigravity isotonic exercises should be stressed. Not only do isotonic exercises result in more physiological benefits, but they also allow the individual to derive the satisfaction of seeing and knowing just how much effort he has put forth. This effort can be judged by the number of times a part of the body has been moved through a range of motion. Furthermore, the participant also knows how much resistance he has overcome. The factor of not knowing just how much effort is being exerted when isometric exercises are performed has certain motivational limitations.

For the following antigravity isotonic exercises, eight to twelve repetitions should be performed. When the individual is able to perform more than twelve repetitions with a given resistance, the resistance should be increased to limit the participant to eight repetitions. As the tolerance for that exercise increases, the resistance should be progressively increased.

Four exercises are suggested for use when particular attention is focused upon development of strength and muscular endurance to aid the individual to assume an erect standing posture. These exercises are (1) sit-up (Fig. 12.45), (2) back-raise (Fig. 12.46), (3) leg extension (Fig. 12.39), and (4) scapular adduction (Fig. 12.31). Each of these exercises is described in detail later in this chapter.

EXERCISE FOR CONGENITAL AND PATHOLOGICAL CONDITIONS

It has been the intention throughout this book to present the fundamental bases and principles upon which sound therapeutic exercise programs can be developed. Many disabilities, particularly those resulting from trauma to the musculoskeletal system, can be grouped in such a way that the individuals may be placed in groups in which similar routines of exercises can be administered to each individual within several subgroups. In the case of congenital and pathological conditions, however, exact similarities of anomalies or malformations are not usually found. This is true, especially in those handicapping conditions that involve deformations of an orthopedic nature. In these situations, very specific classifications and recommendations are generally made. The wide variation in the prescriptions for exercises requires that the "routine" method of administering exercises should not be utilized in most instances. Thus, the exercises for these disabilities will necessitate numerous modifications to meet specific requirements for each condition. This situation is one where the possession of a thorough knowledge of the principles of therapeutic exercise becomes indispensable to the adapted physical education teacher.

There are some conditions which have as their end result a debilitating effect on the individual. For example, extended bed rest may cause extreme atrophy of the total musculature of the body. The physical fitness of the individual may be improved through the use of routinely administered progressive-resistance exercises. For example, asthmatic students may benefit from such a program. A general conditioning program is presented and described in another section of this chapter.

It should be remembered that not all physically handicapping conditions will respond to or, for that matter, require exercise. Even though the individual may be enrolled in an adapted physical education class, his medical recommendation might be for him to rest. Some individuals require relaxation or an opportunity to be inactive during the physical education period. For example, the student with a cardiac problem who has a tendency to overexert himself may profit from a period of inactivity. It would give him an opportunity to recover from the effects of his previous exertion. Therefore, if the medical recommendation is for the individual to rest during the adapted physical education class, the success of the program in relation to that individual will depend upon adequate rest during the physical education class.

The sports phase of the adapted physical education program has a wide application for many students with congenital and pathological conditions. It is important that the individual participate in recreational sports and games which are appropriate to his capabilities and limitations. Specific suggestions and recommendations for programming may be found in Chapter 9.

APPLIED EXERCISE FOR TRAUMATIC CONDITIONS

The use of therapeutic exercise as a rehabilitative measure has recently been accepted on a widespread scale. Strength-developing exercise is one of the major tools in the adapted physical education program. The major stabilizers of the joints are the muscles. Ligaments serve to hold the joints together, but they are primarily limiting structures at the extremes of the range of motion. Once they have become elongated or stretched beyond their normal length, it becomes necessary to substitute increased strength of the muscles spanning the joints. The most common injuries to the joints are sprains and dislocations. These injuries also result in the tearing of other limiting joint structures in addition to the ligaments. No matter what structures are involved in the injury, inactivity will result in muscle atrophy. Therefore, following almost every type of joint injury, some form of strength-developing exercise may be prescribed. The exercise routines suggested for the ankle, knee, back, shoulder, and elbow are designed for the development of strength. The purpose of this strength development is to increase the stability of the joints in these involved areas.

The procedure for the use of these exercises is based upon DeLorme's[6] progressive-resistance exercise described in Chapter 11. Referral should be made to that section of the book before using the exercises.

A knowledge of joint movement is essential to the most effective application of exercise for therapeutic purposes. If a part of the body is moved through all of its possible ranges of motion, all of the muscles that act upon the joint involved are being strengthened. Therefore, the selection of strength exercises must be based upon a thorough consideration of the possible joint movements. The following exercise routines were developed largely on the basis of this principle.

Ankle

Difficulty in the attachment of resistance to the foot arises when attempting to increase strength of the muscles that stabilize the ankle joint. Some type of device is required to which resistance can be added. Such a device[7] is shown in Figure 12.15. The foot is strapped into a foot plate which can be pivoted so that the lever arm to which weights are attached may be placed at the four positions for exercise of the ankle. These positions are with the lever arm to the front, back, and sides of the ankle. When weight is placed on the lever arm, the foot is moved upward against the resistance. Additional weights are added as the tolerance for the exercise increases. If no device is available, the most satisfactory way to exercise these lateral stabilizing muscles is for the individual to perform heel raises with weights placed on his shoulders. In this exercise, the individual raises his body plus the weight up and down

6 Thomas L. DeLorme and Arthur L. Watkins, *Progressive Resistance Exercise* (New York: Appleton-Century-Crofts, Inc., 1951).

7 Designed by the authors.

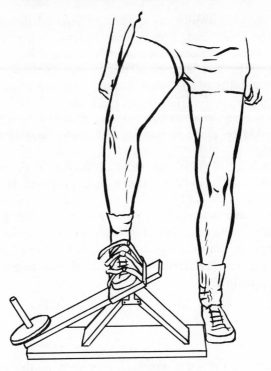

Figure 12.15

while standing on the balls of his feet. The resistance should be increased progressively. This exercise should be avoided by individuals with a tendency toward weak longitudinal arches. Although this exercise is not specific for the lateral stabilizing muscles, they are involved in the action. As a result, they are strengthened in the process. The movements of eversion and inversion of the foot require that a lever of some type be attached to the foot for proper application of resistance. Therefore, an ankle-exercising device is essential when these specific movements are to be performed most efficiently.

In Figure 12.15 the foot is in the starting position for exercising the everters on the lateral side of the ankle. The lever arm is raised as high as possible by the everters. Care should be taken to

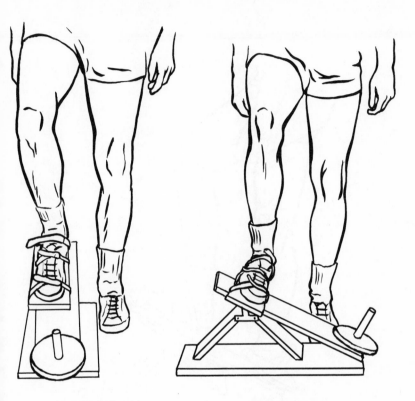

Figure 12.16   **Figure 12.17**

avoid a downward push with the medial side of the foot. This exercise for the lateral stabilizers is done in accordance with the progressive-resistance-exercise procedures described previously.

Figure 12.16 shows the ankle in the starting position for exercising the dorsiflexor muscles. The lever is raised as high as possible while avoiding downward pressure on the heel. This exercise is for the anterior stabilizers.

Figure 12.17 indicates the starting position for exercising the inverters. The lever is raised as high as possible. Pressure on the lateral side of the foot should be avoided. This exercise is for the medial stabilizers of the ankle.

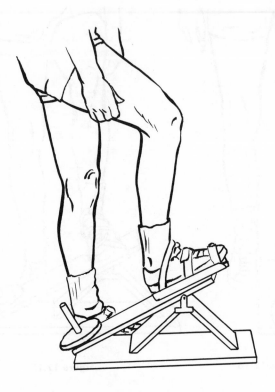

Figure 12.18

Figure 12.18 shows the starting position for exercising the plantar-flexor muscles. The lever is raised as high as possible while avoiding downward pressure on the front of the foot. Since this exercise involves a strong muscle group, more resistance will be required here than for the other three exercises for the ankle. If more resistance is required than can be added to the ankle-exercising device, the individual should place a weight on his shoulders and perform heel-raising exercises as mentioned previously. This exercise is designed to increase strength in the posterior stabilizers of the ankle.

Knee

The knee joint is dependent largely upon muscle support for its stability. If the muscles become atrophied and weakened after an injury, the joint is susceptible to further injury. Since pain reduces the desire to move a part, it can be seen that a number of factors are operating that result in further disuse. Strengthening exercises are absolutely essential for proper rehabilitation. Furthermore, strength of the muscles crossing the knee joint is also basic for the prevention of recurring knee disabilities.

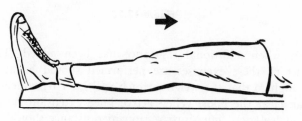

Figure 12.19

When pain and swelling permit, exercises consisting of repeatedly tensing the extensor muscles (quadriceps), as illustrated in Figure 12.19, should be performed for five minutes of each waking hour. If the individual has difficulty in tensing the quadriceps at the outset, this action may be started by having him attempt to pull the patella upward. He can also attempt to push down on the back of the knee. This exercise should be executed with the knee as straight as possible.

Active extension of the knee should be started as soon as permissible. The starting position for active extension of the knee is shown in Figure 12.20. The reader should note that a sponge leatherette-covered pad is attached to the table being used. This pad is for the prevention of discomfort during knee extension, par-

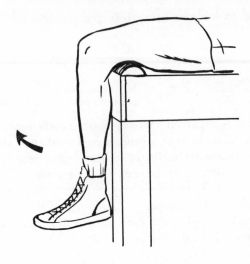

Figure 12.20

ticularly when additional resistance has been added. The table upon which these exercises are performed should be at least 36 inches high so that the weights which will later be attached to the foot can clear the floor. When active knee extension can be completed at least ten times, progression in resistance should be made by adding weight to the foot.

A 5-pound iron boot strapped to the foot is shown in Figure 12.21. An iron bar is placed through this boot, to which metal plates can be attached when greater resistance is required (Fig. 12.22). On each repetition, the knee should be held momentarily at complete extension. (The degree of extension will vary in proportion to the strength of the quadriceps.) The lower leg should then be lowered to the starting position. The exercise should be continued as recommended previously.

When the injured knee reaches the strength of the other knee, weights should be attached to both feet. Both knee extensors can be increased in strength at the same time. It is important to maintain a balanced increase in strength for more normal functioning of the knee joint.

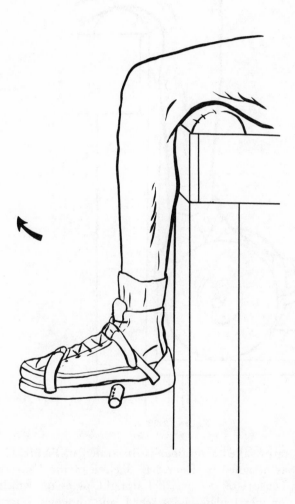

Figure 12.21

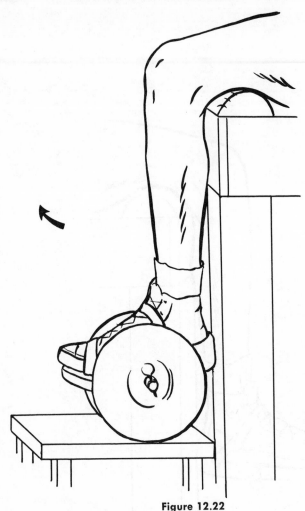

Figure 12.22

An apparatus called a *pressbar* is illustrated in Figure 12.23. This device was designed by Robert E. Shelton of the University of Illinois. It consists of two parallel upright pipes on which a movable bar for metal plates is attached, and provides a means for exercising the three major stabilizing muscle groups of the knee at the same time. The plantar-flexors of the ankle and the extensors of the hip are also exercised with this device. The starting position

Figure 12.23

is shown. Metal pins are placed in holes in the parallel upright pipes just below the movable unit for added safety. The pipes on the movable sleeve just below the crossbar are approximately 14 inches long in order to prevent the crossbar from falling on the individual if the feet slip during the exercise.

To begin the exercise, the individual lies on his back with the lower border of his rib cage approximately in line with the crossbar. This position prevents the knees from going into complete flexion. The lower limbs should be kept parallel to each other, and the knees should not be allowed to spread apart. If the knees should spread apart on knee flexion, injury might occur. Furthermore, if the sacrum rises from the floor in the starting position, the individual should move so that the crossbar is below the lower border of the rib cage. The balls of the feet should be placed on the crossbar with the feet approximately 6 inches apart. The metal pins are then removed, and the hands are placed along the sides. A four-count rhythm is recommended for the exercise: (1) the knees should be straightened; (2) the feet are pressed as high as possible (plantar-flexed); (3) the feet are then lowered (dorsiflexed) as far as possible

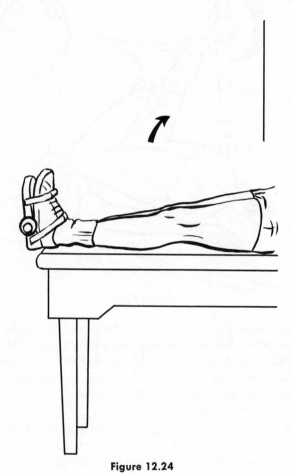

Figure 12.24

while the knees are still straight; and (4) the crossbar should be lowered slowly to the starting position. The use of this device is recommended for the later stages of the rehabilitative progressive-resistance-exercise program.

Hip

Infrequently, therapeutic exercise will be recommended for common disabilities of the hip. Light weights are usually necessary, because the lower limb provides a long lever arm which prevents the lifting of greater resistance. An iron boot strapped to the foot is shown in Figure 12.24. The lower limb is raised to the line indicated, and lowered slowly to the starting position. This exercise is primarily for the hip flexors. The exercise should be continued according to previously outlined procedures.

The starting position for exercising the hip extensors is shown in Figure 12.25. An iron boot is secured to the foot of one lower limb. In order to stabilize the trunk when the weight is lifted, the individual should grasp the table.

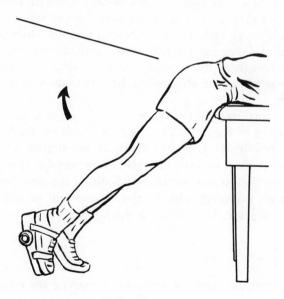

Figure 12.25

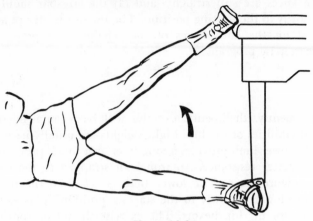

Figure 12.26

The starting position for increasing the strength of the adductor muscles of the hip is shown in Figure 12.26. The unaffected lower limb rests on a table. This position provides optimum range of motion for adduction of the affected part. The lower limb should be raised as high as possible and lowered slowly to the starting position. If a table is not available on which to rest the uninvolved lower limb, it may be held in position while the affected lower limb is being exercised. However, maintaining stability of the trunk is difficult in this position. As a substitute for this exercise, pulley weights may be attached to the foot to provide the necessary resistance.

The starting position for strengthening the abductors of the hip is shown in Figure 12.27. The lower limb should be abducted as far as possible and lowered slowly to the starting position. Exercises for the hip rotators may also be performed. However, positioning for the exercise is rather difficult. If the four previous hip exercises are executed properly, the rotators will be sufficiently involved to increase the stability of the hip joint.

Back

Recommendations for therapeutic exercise for common back disabilities may range from very mild to quite strenuous progressive-resistance exercises. The exercise would depend upon the con-

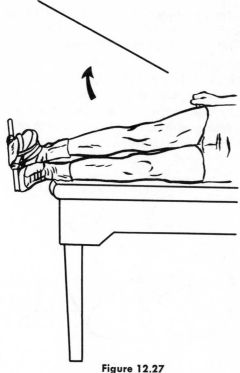

Figure 12.27

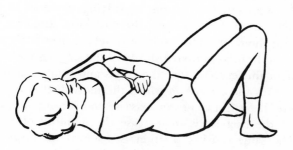

Figure 12.28

dition of the back disability and the tolerance of the individual for exercise. The following routine of exercises is often recommended for acute back disabilities. The first of these exercises is illustrated in Figure 12.28. The knees should be flexed as shown to flatten the lumbar area against the supporting surface. The upper limbs are folded across the chest. The abdominal and gluteal muscles should be contracted simultaneously to cause the pelvis to rotate and force the lumbar spine downward. This position should be held momentarily and the exercise repeated. The number of repetitions that the individual can perform will depend upon his tolerance. Some students may not be able to complete ten repetitions at the outset of the exercise program. The major purpose of this exercise is to decrease the lumbar curvature while strengthening the muscles indicated.

Figure 12.29

An abdominal-strengthening exercise is illustrated in Figure 12.29. The individual is in the hook-lying position as for the previous exercise. In this exercise, the individual attempts to raise his head and shoulders. This position is held momentarily, and the shoulders and head are lowered slowly to the starting position. It is important in this exercise that the pelvis and lumbar area remain in contact with the surface on which the individual is lying.

Figure 12.30 illustrates an exercise for the hip flexors. The purpose of the exercise is to increase the mobility of the pelvic region. The same starting position is assumed as shown for the two previous exercises. The knee of one leg should be brought up toward the chest as far as possible, held there momentarily, then lowered slowly to the starting position. This procedure should be repeated alternately with the other leg until the hip flexors on both sides have been exercised ten times.

Figure 12.30

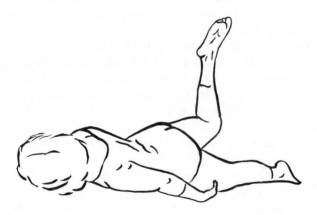

Figure 12.31

An exercise for strengthening the hip extensors is illustrated in Figure 12.31. The individual begins the exercise in a prone position with one knee flexed approximately 90 degrees. The lower limb is raised to the position indicated and returned to the starting position. The exercise is then executed for the other lower limb. This exercise is continued until ten repetitions have been performed with both lower limbs. At the beginning of each attempt to raise the knee from the surface, the individual should also contract the abdominal muscles so that very little increase in lumbar curvature will occur during the exercise.

Figure 12.32

The last of this routine of exercises is illustrated in Figure 12.32. It is a gluteal-strengthening exercise often called gluteal "pinching." With the individual in the position shown, an attempt is made to contract the gluteal muscles forcefully. They should be held in this state momentarily, and then they should be allowed to relax. Tightening the abdominal muscles at the same time adds to the benefits of this exercise.

Once this routine of rather mild exercises can be performed easily, it is usually recommended that more strenuous progressive-resistance exercises be used. As the acute stage of the back disability subsides, progressive-resistance exercises are given that impose greater demands. Because of the large and potentially powerful muscle groups such as the erector spinae, exertions of high magnitude are required to increase strength and to improve stability in this vital region. The exercises described above are often recommended for long-term usage. They can adequately serve the needs of some individuals. However, more strenuous exercises are required for most *chronic* or long-term common disabilities of the back.

The following exercises were adapted from a series called the *Shelton Back Routine*. They were designed by Robert E. Shelton for common disabilities of the back following the acute stage. For best results, these exercises should be performed in the sequence indicated. Since they are designed to develop both strength *and* endurance, the procedures for the applications of progressive resistance recommended for the other routines in this section of the book are modified. It is recommended that each exercise be performed for a maximum of twenty consecutive repetitions. If this number of repetitions can be performed, additional resistance in the form of metal plates should be held behind the head or secured between the ankles with a strap. Placement of the resistance would depend upon the exercise. For example, if the exercise can be done for twenty repetitions with the addition of 5 pounds, the weight should be increased to 10 pounds. This amount is considered a maximum weight for this routine of exercises, because the addition of further resistance may be beyond the limits of safety.

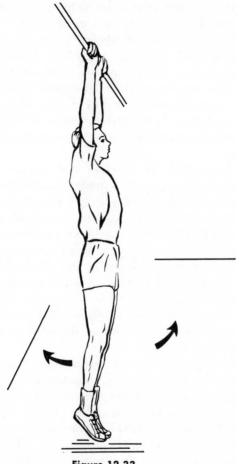

Figure 12.33

The first and second exercises of this routine are illustrated in Figure 12.33. The first exercise involves a passive hang from an overhead bar. The bar should be high enough for the feet to clear the floor. The purpose of this exercise is to promote muscular relaxation and passive stretching. The individual should increase his tolerance for this exercise to a maximum of one minute of passive hanging. The second exercise of the series is called an *active hang.* The objective of the exercise is to increase the strength and endurance of the anterior and posterior trunk muscles. The exercise is started from a hanging position. The lower limbs are brought forward to the line indicated, held momentarily, then lowered to the active hang position. The second phase of the exercise is to move the lower limbs from the active-hang position backward to the line indicated, hold momentarily, then return to the starting position. These movements should be executed without swinging or relying on momentum. The full cycle of this exercise is considered one repetition. This exercise is rather difficult for individuals with low tolerance. Nevertheless, an attempt should be made to do the exercise.

A straight-legged sit-up exercise is illustrated in Figure 12.34. The purpose of this exercise is to strengthen the abdominal muscles. With the feet held down by a strap or by *stall bars* (a rubber automobile innertube placed around the top of the table serves this purpose well), the fingers are clasped together behind the head. The individual then comes up to a sitting position. A return is then made to the starting position, and the exercise is repeated. The lower limbs should be kept as straight as possible; however, some bending is unavoidable in most instances. When the ability to perform twenty repetitions is reached, a 5-pound metal plate is placed in the hands and held behind the head. Progression is then made as described previously.

The straight-legged sit-up exercise should not be attempted by individuals with weak abdominal muscles. The level of weakness is determined by whether or not the abdominals can maintain the proper relationship between the pubis and the rib cage when the exercise is being executed. If the curvature of the lumbar spine tends to increase at the beginning of this exercise, then the abdominal muscles have insufficient strength to perform this exercise properly.

Although one of the hip flexors, the psoas major, primarily performs flexion at the hip and flexion of the lumbar spine, it may at times serve as a hyperextensor of the lumbar spine. This function of hyperextension may occur when the lower limbs are held sta-

Figure 12.34

tionary and the individual attempts to perform a sit-up, especially in the presence of weakened abdominal muscles. This reversal of function of the psoas muscle is known as the *psoas paradox*.[8] It is recommended that sit-ups be done with the knees and hips in a flexed position to help avoid this situation. Once the abdominal muscles have become strong enough to maintain the proper relationships, progression can be made to the straight-legged sit-up exercise.

[8] Philip J. Rasch and Roger K. Burke, *Kinesiology and Applied Anatomy*, 2nd ed. (Philadelphia: Lea & Febinger, 1963) p. 341.

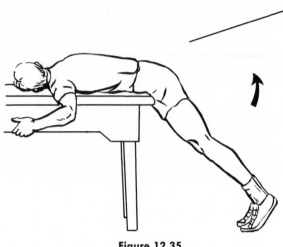

Figure 12.35

A prone position with the hands grasping the underside of a table is assumed for the prone double-leg-raise exercise illustrated in Figure 12.35. The extensors of the hip and the back are exercised. The lower limbs will be raised simultaneously to the point indicated by the line in the illustration. The knees should be kept as straight as possible. Swing or the use of momentum should be avoided in this exercise. When twenty repetitions can be performed, a 5-pound plate should be strapped between the ankles. The exercise is then continued according to the previous description.

An exercise primarily for the abdominal muscles is illustrated in Figure 12.36. The starting position is assumed with the feet anchored as indicated. The trunk is curled up to a sitting position. When twenty repetitions can be performed, a 5-pound plate should be placed behind the head during the exercise. Progression should be made as noted previously.

The last back exercise is illustrated in Figure 12.37. This is an exercise for the hip and back extensors. The exercise should start with the feet anchored and the hands clasped behind the head. The trunk is then raised to the line indicated or as high as possible, held momentarily, then lowered slowly to the starting position. When twenty repetitions can be performed, an iron plate weighing

Figure 12.36

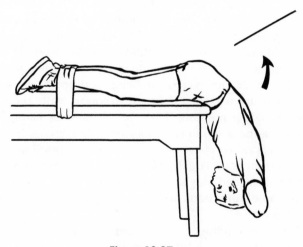

Figure 12.37

5 pounds should be held behind the head. The exercise is continued according to the procedure described previously. The head should be raised as high as possible. This exercise is called a *prone trunk raise*.

These exercises are basically *bilateral* exercises. The movements should be performed only through one plane of motion, the anterior-posterior. If, for example, when a prone trunk raise is being executed, one shoulder may tend to come up before the other. This movement has a rotary component. The individual should be instructed to move so that the shoulders remain level throughout the movement. In this way, a better-balanced muscle function is attained. Often the imbalance of muscular strength results in an inability of the individual to perform movement through one plane of motion. Therefore, great emphasis should be placed upon symmetrical development through an anterior-posterior range of motion.

Shoulder

The exercises that compose the shoulder routine are designed specifically for the rehabilitation of shoulder dislocations. The main difference between a rehabilitation program for dislocations and that for other common shoulder disabilities is that in exercises for the prevention of recurrent shoulder dislocations, the upper limb is never allowed to be raised above shoulder level. If the upper limb is raised above this level, there is a very high possibility of dislocation while the exercise is being performed, particularly in such movements as raising a weight overhead while the individual is in the standing position. Therefore, it must be emphasized that in rehabilitating a shoulder dislocation, all exercises in which the upper limb is raised above shoulder level are contraindicated. This routine of exercises is equally effective for other common disabilities of the shoulder, and may serve as a starting point in the rehabilitation of those conditions other than dislocations at the glenohumeral joint.

A passive circling exercise used for loosening the involved structures around the joint during the initial stages of rehabilita-

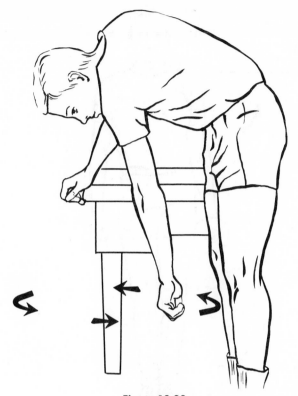

Figure 12.38

tion of the shoulder joint is indicated in Figure 12.38. This movement should be performed several times, depending upon the
tolerance of the individual in terms of pain and range of motion.
A large circle should be described with the hand while the upper
limb is hanging relaxed. Movements should be clockwise as well as
counterclockwise.

As the tolerance for resistance exercise increases, an exercise
for the abductors of the shoulder should be performed as indicated
in Figure 12.39. The exercise should be started without resistance
other than the upper limb itself raised to the line indicated and
then lowered to the starting position. Progression should then be
made on the basis of the progressive-resistance exercise techniques

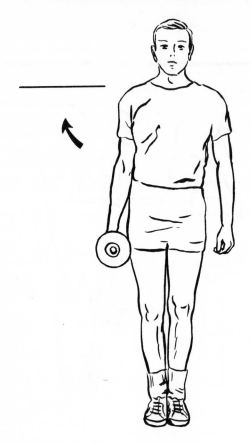

Figure 12.39

described previously for strength development. Resistance in the form of dumbbells or other objects held in the hand are recommended. Once the amount of weight that can be lifted is equal to the amount that can be lifted by the unaffected shoulder, the exercise should be done bilaterally, with a weight held in each hand. Abduction may then be done with both shoulders to help maintain symmetry of the muscles in the areas involved.

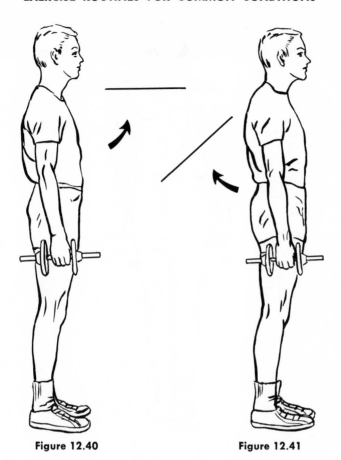

Figure 12.40   **Figure 12.41**

An exercise for the forward flexors of the shoulders is illustrated in Figure 12.40. The upper limb should be raised to the line indicated, held momentarily, and lowered to the starting position. All movements should be executed without swing or momentum.

An exercise for the muscles which hyperextend the upper limb is shown in Figure 12.41. The upper limb should be moved backward as far as possible while the individual maintains an erect posture. The exercise should be repeated as suggested previously.

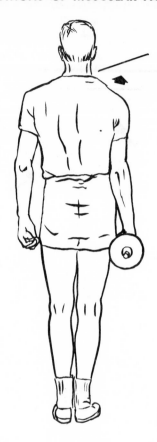

Figure 12.42

An exercise for the elevators of the shoulder girdle is illustrated in Figure 12.42. It is generally called a *shoulder shrug,* and it is performed by a "hiking" action of the shoulder girdle. Greater resistance may be required for this exercise than for the others indicated in this routine.

In order to exercise the horizontal adductor muscles of the shoulder, it is necessary that the individual lie on a narrow, padded bench. This position allows the upper limb to be in the position

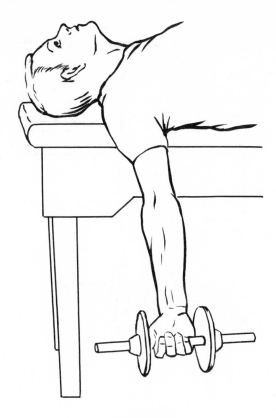

Figure 12.43

indicated in Figure 12.43. From this starting position, the upper limb is raised to a vertical position, held momentarily, then lowered to the starting position. By allowing the upper limb to go as low to the floor as possible, extensibility of the pectoral muscles is enhanced. Some flexion at the elbow during the exercise is suggested in order to stabilize that joint. Thus, more resistance can be applied to the shoulder joint.

With the individual in a face-down position (Fig. 12.44), an exercise for the scapular adductors is performed. The scapular ad-

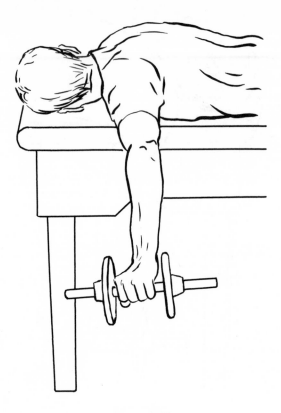

Figure 12.44

ductor muscles will be activated, and the muscles which perform horizontal abduction of the shoulder will also be activated. Again, the exercise should be performed without swing or momentum. It is particularly important in this exercise for the individual to raise the upper limb with the resistance as high as possible on each repetition. This is also an excellent postural exercise.

An exercise for the rotators of the shoulder is illustrated in Figure 12.45. The starting position for this exercise is indicated. Note that the elbow is flexed 90 degrees. The shoulder is abducted to 90 degrees. The anterior aspect of the elbow joint should be in

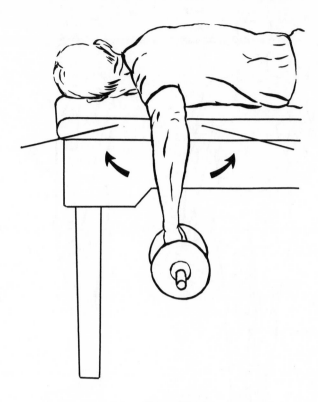

Figure 12.45

contact with the edge of the bench. The forearm should be raised to the lines indicated in the illustration. It is particularly important that the upper arm be rotated on its longitudinal axis. Adduction and abduction of this part should not be performed. Also, the weight used for resistance should not be raised above the level of the shoulder. In externally rotating the upper arm, it may *appear* that this principle is contradicted; but it should be remembered that the *upper* arm should not be raised above shoulder level. This type of exercise should not be executed in any other position than that illustrated in Figure 12.45.

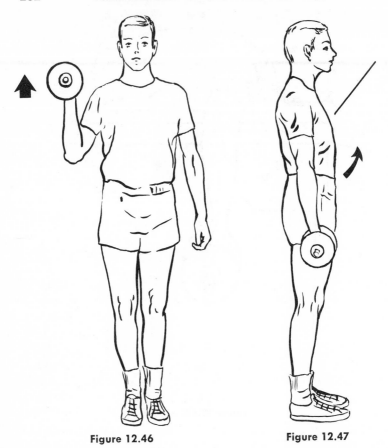

Figure 12.46   **Figure 12.47**

A progressive-resistance exercise for increasing the strength of the flexors of the elbow joint is shown in Figure 12.46. This exercise is called a *biceps curl*. When the strength of the involved upper limb reaches that of the other upper limb, the exercise should be continued with a barbell, utilizing both upper limbs. In performing this exercise, it is suggested that the individual stand with his back against a wall. His heels should be approximately 6 inches from the wall to prevent swinging of the body backward when the exercise is executed. The proper body position places maximum stress on the musculature being strengthened.

The starting position for an exercise to strengthen the elbow extensors is shown in Figure 12.47. The weight should be pressed overhead and lowered to the starting position. When the strength of the involved upper limb reaches that of the uninvolved upper limb, the exercise should be done with both upper limbs. This exercise is sometimes called an *overhead press*. It is described in the section containing a general conditioning program.

Neck

Sprains and strains to the cervico-thoracic region, are becoming more and more prevalent as a result of automobile accidents. These injuries often occur when an automobile in which the individual is sitting is hit from the rear.

After the acute symptoms are relieved by any one or a combination of other therapeutic measures, an exercise regimen is usually begun. The following exercises were suggested by Leila C. Randall, Physical Therapist, Student Health Service, University of Southern California, and consist of contracting the neck muscles in all planes against resistance applied by the individual's own hand or hands. In some cases, the objective is to develop muscular strength. More commonly, it is used to relieve the pain of muscle "tension." Following this injury, the individual often complains of severe headache. This headache frequently interferes with his attention to matters, particularly for a student in a classroom. These exercises can be performed in an inconspicuous way because they are basically isometric exercises which can be repeated several times against the individual's own maximum resistance.

The performance of these neck-strengthening exercises is relatively simple. Sitting at a classroom desk with the forehead resting in the hand, the forehead is pressed against the hand. Next, with the elbow resting on the desk and the hand against the side of the face, the individual forcefully attempts to turn the head to the right and then to the left. The face is pressed alternately toward the hand which offers the resistance. No movement of the head should be allowed.

The next exercise is with the fingers clasped together behind the head. Without any movement, the head should be forced back toward the hands. The procedure should be repeated several times. Empirical observation indicates that this procedure is extremely effective, particularly in a classroom, where "tension" in the cervico-thoracic region often develops from the position required for note taking.

GENERAL-CONDITIONING PROGRAM

The following general-conditioning routine of exercises is devised for those individuals requiring developmental exercises. It is a selected series of exercises which are designed for the development of strength, endurance, and flexibility. Many other exercises could be included here, but those that are included are considered basic to any general-conditioning program. If further exercises are desired, the reader should refer to an exercise book.[9]

The principles for the development of strength, endurance, and flexibility are detailed in Chapter 11. The suggestion was made there that gross body-movement exercises should be performed prior to other types of specific exercise. This practice enhances general body warm-up. Increasing the rate and duration of this type of exercise also results in better endurance because of an improvement in the function of the circulatory-respiratory mechanism.

If this series of general-conditioning exercises is used in conjunction with a posture program, caution should be taken not to strengthen muscles already overdeveloped in respect to their antagonists. Attention should be paid to the provision of a balance of strength between antagonists for those attempting to correct certain common postural deviations.

After a sufficient warm-up, flexibility exercises should be included to increase the range of motion in the areas in which limitation of movement frequently occurs because of inactivity. These exercises should be repeated slowly five to ten times. "Bouncing" should be avoided. Execute all exercises without swing or

9 Earl L. Wallis and Gene A. Logan, *Figure Improvement and Body Conditioning through Exercise* (Englewood Cliffs, N.J.: Prentice-Hall, Inc., 1964).

Figure 12.48

momentum. The strength-development procedures follow the circulatory-respiratory warm-up and flexibility exercises. These exercises should be performed according to the procedures outlined in Chapter 11. The number of repetitions should remain between eight and twelve. When the individual is able to perform more than twelve repetitions, more resistance should be applied.

A *side-straddle-hop* warm-up exercise involving the total body is shown in Figure 12.48. A commonly used exercise, increasing its rate and number of repetitions will bring about a rapid elevation of circulatory responses. The lower limbs should be spread as far as possible. The upper limbs are swung overhead in unison with the movement of the lower limbs. This exercise may be varied. For example, the student can swing the upper limbs and lower limbs forward and backward to involve specific muscle groups.

Figure 12.49

A warm-up exercise involving the lower trunk and lower limbs is shown in Figure 12.49. From a "push-up" position with the arms held straight, the knees and hips should be alternately flexed and extended. The rate of performance should be increased as the tolerance of the individual increases. During the exercise, the hands should remain in the starting position.

Many different exercises may be used for increasing the flexibility of the posterior supporting structures of the body. However, a safe exercise for this purpose, and one that prevents the individual from applying too much force, is indicated in Figure 12.50. The individual assumes the position indicated in the illustration with the hands flat on the floor and the fingers pointing forward. To execute the exercise, the lower limbs are straightened while the hands remain in contact with the floor. An attempt

Figure 12.50

should then be made to force the knees gently into extension. At the same time, control of the movement should be maintained to prevent undue stress. Muscular stress is often encountered in many forward bending exercises involving the weight of the trunk in a rapid motion. The exercise should be repeated five to ten times.

An exercise for promoting flexibility of the upper back and neck is shown in Figure 12.51. The individual begins the exercise while lying in a supine position. The lower limbs are then lifted slowly overhead as indicated. It is important that the hips be as far over the head as possible. An attempt should be made to touch the toes to the floor. Forcing the hands downward helps the individual to assume this position. An alternate procedure, which involves almost the same movement, is for the lower limbs to be held in the air, then alternately flexed and extended while the hips are supported by the hands. This alternate exercise, generally called a "bicycle" exercise, may also be used for warm-up prior to other types of activity. At the same time, it can be used for increasing flexibility of the areas indicated. This exercise should be avoided by individuals with common anterior-posterior postural deviations,

Figure 12.51

as it is likely that overextensibility of these structures is already present.

The following eight exercises are designed primarily for the development of strength. The progressive-resistance exercise procedures outlined previously should be used when performing these exercises.

An exercise for the extensors of the ankles, knees, hips, and lower back is shown in Figure 12.52. The position shown should be assumed with the lower limbs straddling the barbell. The hands are well spread to permit a balanced placement of the weight. The back should be held as straight as possible throughout the exercise. When the weight is lifted, the action should be at the ankles, knees, and hips only. Back movement should be held to a minimum. This exercise is less hazardous than the often used "squat" exercise in which the barbell is placed across the shoulders. Also, assistance is not required to place the weight on the shoulders at the beginning of the exercise and to remove it at the termination of the exercise. No jerking or rapid forceful movement should be allowed at any time during this or any other of the strength-developing exercises suggested in any of these routines.

Figure 12.52

Figure 12.53

A *bench-press* exercise for the development of the muscles of the upper limbs and chest is illustrated in Figure 12.53. The pectoral and triceps muscles primarily are involved. When the tolerance of the individual has begun to increase, assistance may be required in order to place the barbell in the starting position.

When heavier resistances are used, spotters are required to assist the individual in the placement and removal of the weight. Care should be taken to maintain an up-and-down rhythmical motion. The termination of the exercise should be at the "up" position. The wider the hands are spread on the bar, the more stress will be placed upon the pectoral muscles. A narrow grip places greater stress on the triceps muscles.

Figure 12.54

An exercise for strengthening the flexors of the elbows is shown in Figure 12.54. The flexors of the wrist are also strengthened in this exercise if wrist action is included with the *biceps curl*. The weight should be held with the hands at shoulder width. The palms face forward with the hands grasping the weight. An alternate position is with the palms facing the individual. This variation provides exercise for muscles not primarily activated in the palm-forward procedure. However, there is very little difference between these two positions in regard to the action that takes place at the elbow joint. Swinging the weight upward by throwing the trunk backward should be avoided. In order to counteract this tendency, it is suggested that the individual stand with his back to a wall. The heels should be approximately 6 inches from the wall. This position prevents backward swinging. It also isolates the movement to the area being exercised.

Figure 12.55

An erect rowing exercise for strengthening the muscles of the shoulders—particularly the deltoids—is illustrated in Figure 12.55. A full range of motion should be stressed as the weight is raised as high as possible. In order to raise the weight to its highest possible point, it is necessary for the elbows to be moved forward ʌnd upward from the starting position. Backward swinging should be avoided. When the exercise is being executed, attention should be paid to correct body alignment, especially in the area of the pelvis. The abdominal muscles should be tensed in such a way as to maintain firm trunk stability throughout the exercise.

Figure 12.56

An *overhead-press* exercise for the development of strength in the shoulder area is shown in Figure 12.56. Execution of this exercise should take place in a sitting position to avoid excessive strain on the low-back area during the movement. The weight should be placed on the bench first. It is then moved into the starting position by the individual before the weight is pressed overhead. Pelvic stability should be maintained throughout the exercise. Although this exercise may be done in the standing position, the sitting position is preferred, because it affords greater safety for those individuals who may have a tendency toward back disabilities.

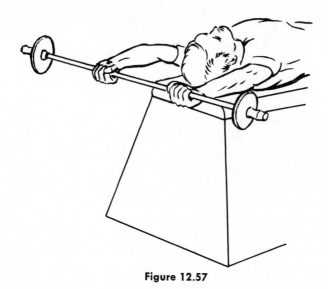

Figure 12.57

A straight-arm *pull-over* exercise for the development of arm and chest strength is shown in Figure 12.57. This exercise also places much stress on the latissimus dorsi muscles—muscles that are difficult to exercise otherwise, except in a *pull-up* or *pull-down* type of exercise. (A pull-down exercise requires the use of a mechanical pulley apparatus. All too often, this apparatus is not available.)

Excessive resistances should be avoided at the initiation of the exercise because the joint structures of the shoulder are in an unfavorable position to maintain their integrity. The weight should be raised in an arc with the upper limbs held in an extended position. Each repetition should terminate when the weight has reached the highest point in the arc. The weight should be lowered to the starting position as illustrated.

Figure 12.58

The two most important exercises basic to any conditioning program are (1) the *sit-up,* involving the abdominal muscles, and (2) the *back-raise,* which exercises the back and leg extensor muscles. The starting position for the sit-up is shown in Figure 12.58. In this position, the knees and hips are flexed and the buttocks are approximately 6 inches from the heels. The feet should be anchored so that maximum stress can be placed on the abdominal muscles. This position provides greater emphasis on the abdominals than if the knees are kept straight. With the knees in a straight position, more stress is placed on the hip flexors than on the abdominal muscles. As the ability to increase the number of repetitions in the sit-up occurs, a weight should be placed behind the head. The weight is held firmly with the hands. The degree of weight should be progressively increased as the tolerance of the individual is elevated.

A strengthening exercise (back-raise) for the extensor muscles of the back and lower limbs is shown in Figure 12.59. With the feet anchored, the fingers should be clasped together behind the head. The trunk is then elevated as high as possible. A momentary hesitation should be made at the highest point in the range of motion. The trunk is then lowered to the starting position. As the tolerance for this exercise is increased, a weight should be placed behind the head for additional resistance. If difficulty is encountered at the outset of the back-raise exercise, it is suggested that the exercise be initiated from a prone-lying position with the feet anchored. The trunk should be raised from that position and lowered again to the

Figure 12.59

starting point. Of all the exercises in this general-conditioning program, the greatest improvement can be expected in the back-raise. This phenomenon suggests that the strength of the back in most people is below that which may be required when maximum effort is desired. It may also partially explain the high incidence of back disabilities in unconditioned individuals.

Selected References

Corrective Physical Education: Teaching Guide for Junior and Senior High Schools. Los Angeles City Schools, Division of Instructional Services, Pub. No. SC-566.

DeLorme, Thomas L., and Arthur L. Watkins, *Progressive Resistance Exercise.* New York: Appleton-Century-Crofts, Inc., 1951.

Licht, Sidney, ed., *Therapeutic Exercise.* New Haven, Conn.: Elizabeth Licht, 1958.

Kraus, Hans, *Principles and Practice of Therapeutic Exercise.* Springfield, Ill.: Charles C Thomas, 1949.

Logan, Gene A., "Instructional Slides for Athletic Training and Rehabilitation." Springfield, Mo.: Box 3535 Glenstone Station.

Logan, Gene A., et al., *Student Handbook for Adapted Physical Education.* Dubuque, Iowa: Wm. C. Brown Co., 1960.

Lowman, Charles LeRoy, et al., *Corrective Physical Education for Groups.* New York: A. S. Barnes and Co., 1928.

Metheny, Eleanor, *Body Dynamics.* New York: McGraw-Hill Book Co., Inc., 1952.

Stafford, George T., and Ellen Davis Kelly, *Preventive and Corrective Physical Education,* 3rd ed. New York: Ronald Press Co., 1958.

Wallis, Earl L., and Gene A. Logan, *Figure Improvement and Body Conditioning through Exercise.* Englewood Cliffs, N.J.: Prentice-Hall, Inc., 1964.

13

SELECTION AND PROGRAMMING OF SPORTS

This chapter is concerned with the selection of games, sports, rhythmic, and aquatic activities to be utilized in the sports phase of the adapted physical education program.

Four categories of forces that affect man's movement and sometimes limit his participation in vigorous physical activity are identified as either congenital or acquired. Those conditions considered in Chapters 8 and 10 which are due either to the force of gravity or to trauma result in musculoskeletal deviations or disabilities. Those congenital and pathological conditions discussed in Chapter 9 affect man's movement through the involvement of either the musculoskeletal or the circulatory and respiratory systems.

Regardless of the specific nature or cause of his physical condition or divergency, the student will benefit from his participation in the adapted physical education program. If—in terms of his individual needs—he either seeks to adapt himself to a permanent condition or requires limited physical activity, he may receive maximum benefit from his participation in the sports phase of the program.

The sports phase of the adapted physical education program

includes sports, games, rhythms, and aquatic activities. This program must offer experiences in a variety of activities to permit students to develop interests and to learn new activities that will give them pleasure and satisfaction in their leisure time.

THE BASES OF SPORTS PROGRAMMING

Acceptance of the belief that adapted physical education must have as its bases (a) the medical diagnosis and recommendation of a physician, (b) the individual needs and interests of the student, and (c) the philosophy of the school implies that these factors play the major roles in the programming of the sports phase of the program for the physically atypical child. The implementation of this belief makes imperative a definite procedure for the physician to communicate his recommendation concerning the limitation of the student's physical activity to the instructor of the adapted program. The diagnosis and recommendation of the physician set the limits of the student's activity within which the instructor is to plan, direct, and supervise the student's participation.

The instructor must also have a comprehensive understanding and knowledge of the student's previous experiences in physical education. He must be aware of these experiences to be able to determine the student's readiness for specific kinds of skill performance. Information gained through conferences with the student concerning his interests in various kinds of physical activities as well as knowledge of the interests and participation of the student's physically "normal" peers in physical education is essential to sound educational planning.

In terms of the school's philosophy, the aim of. the adapted physical education program is to prepare the student for his return to and his participation in the regular physical education program of the school. The sports phase of the adapted program must make maximum use of the activities of the regular physical education program. Therefore, a comparison of the kinds of activities used in the sports phase of the adapted program and those used in the regular physical education program should show little, if any, difference. However, as a result of the possible motor retardation of some of the handicapped children and their lack of previous motor or physical education participation, it is not unusual to have some specialized activities included in the adapted program.

Thus, two questions to ask in planning a program for the handicapped child are (1) "What activities are his peers doing?" and (2) "How can the child participate in the same or similar activities?" In planning the program, one must consider what the child can do in spite of or within the limits of his physical limitations. The major problem confronting the instructor in planning the sports program for the handicapped centers around the phrase "adaptation of the regular physical education activities."

Adaptation of the activities of the regular physical education program for the handicapped involves studying each individual's interests, aptitudes, and abilities. Although these are important, the most difficult phase in the adaptation of physical activities centers around three limitations frequently imposed by his physical condition. These are (1) lack of muscular strength, (2) lack of range of movement of joints, and (3) lack of neuromuscular coordination.

The best procedure for planning the sports program is to select activities that are suited to the particular students enrolled. Not only does the nature of a student's condition affect the selection of specific activities, but it must also be considered in the establishment of individual and group objectives for the students. It is generally accepted that an educational program is more than a question of the selection of specific experiences or activities. An educational program also involves objectives and, more important, the achievement of the objectives.

It must always be kept in mind that the selected activities should be adjusted to the capacity of the individual child. Since the physically atypical or handicapped child has had plenty of failures with which to contend, his play should provide many opportunities for success. Although these successes may be small and gradual, they can provide joy, encouragement, and motivation. These are necessary for the persistence and patience that is required for optimum development. If it were possible to develop a formula for the selection of physical activities for all atypical children, it would include a significant challenge, the hope for success, individual satisfaction, and group approval. The process of helping the child come to a place where he is in reach of success is the task of education. The teacher helps, but progress must be made through the individual's own effort.

CRITERIA FOR THE SELECTION OF ACTIVITIES

The importance of the proper selection of physical education activities for the handicapped child should not be minimized. These activities are one of the child's means of continuing his development or reeducation when the developmental continuity has been interrupted.

The selection of activities to be included in the physical education program for handicapped children should be made on the basis of two general groups of criteria. The first is that all activities should satisfy the basic criteria required of any sound physical education curriculum. The second group includes those criteria which should be followed in the specific selection of activities for physically handicapped children: (1) activities which are appropriate to the student's age and interest, (2) activities which are in accordance with the physician's specific recommendations, (3) activities which are within the limits of the student's disability, (4) activities which do not require extensive adaptation of rules or major changes in the nature of the activity, and (5) activities which are applicable to the greatest number of students with regard to their various physical limitations.

The utilization of the previously mentioned criteria should produce a sports program that will best meet the needs of those students assigned to this phase of the adapted classes. Such a program may be characterized as one in which the activities are chosen because they contribute to the development of the basic factors of human movement or motor performance. These factors may be identified as muscular strength, endurance, flexibility, relaxation, and neuromuscular coordination.

The program should provide for gradual progression from the simplest level of performance that the individual's condition and previous experience permits to the highest level of performance that he is able to achieve. The program should stress the teaching of fundamental skills since many students have not had an opportunity to develop skill in the various activities. Sports with carry-over value should be stressed, and students should be taught that they can use these sports throughout their lifetimes. Furthermore, the students should be given some insight into the benefits to be derived from participating in the various sports.

Only those activities which have a minimum of injury expectation and which will not aggravate the individual's condition should be selected. To this end, the selection of the activities must be based on the individual characteristics of each student.

Although the selection of activities must be made on an individual basis, every effort should be directed to provide experience in a variety of dual, group, or team games and sports. It is through participation in group activities that the individual is afforded the best opportunity for the development of desirable social characteristics that stimulate group identification, recognition, and approval. Therefore, group activity should be a goal of the sports program. The socializing benefits of the activities should be stressed. The students should learn to play with as well as against other persons.

The values of the handicapped student's participation in the carefully selected activities in the sports phase of the program are many. The activities may provide one form of relief from the tension of modern living and a momentary rearrangement of the student's emotional life. The child may secure satisfaction often denied in other areas of life through his participation in muscular activities. In addition, the socializing benefits of physical activities are needed by the handicapped so that he may be temporarily released from the usual cares of daily living.

The ultimate goal of the adapted physical education program is to return the handicapped student to the regular physical education program. Therefore, the sports phase of the program must provide the opportunity for the student to develop and utilize those interests, understandings, and skills which will permit him to participate safely and successfully with his nonhandicapped peers.

Selected References

Corrective Physical Education: Teaching Guide for Junior and Senior High Schools. Los Angeles City Schools, Division of Instructional Services, Pub. No. SC-566.

Daniels, Arthur S., *Adapted Physical Education*. New York: Harper & Row, Publishers, 1954.

Fait, Hollis F., *Adapted Physical Education*. Philadelphia: W. B. Saunders Co., 1960.

Howland, Ivalclare Sprow, *Adapted Physical Education in Schools*. Dubuque, Iowa: Wm. C. Brown Co., 1959.

Hunt, Valerie, *Recreation for the Handicapped*. Englewood Cliffs, N.J.: Prentice-Hall, Inc., 1955.

Klafs, Carl E., "Rhythmic Activities for Handicapped Children," paper presented to the Southwest District Convention, American Association for Health, Physical Education and Recreation, Long Beach, California, 1957.

Mathews, Donald K., Robert Kruse, and Virginia Shaw, *The Science of Physical Education for Handicapped Children*. New York: Harper & Row, Publishers, 1962.

Stafford, George T., *Sports for the Handicapped*. 2nd ed. Englewood Cliffs, N.J.: Prentice-Hall, Inc., 1947.

Stone, Eleanor B., and John W. Deyton, *Corrective Therapy for the Handicapped Child*. Englewood Cliffs, N.J.: Prentice-Hall, Inc., 1951.

14

ORGANIZATION OF THE ADAPTED PROGRAM

The effectiveness of any instructional program is greatly influenced by the nature and scope of its organization and of its administration. Although these two phases of program planning are often treated synonymously, there are significant differences that must be considered.

Organization concerns that phase of educational planning that attempts to discover and answer questions concerning the nature and scope of the proposed program. It considers such broad areas as (1) the need for the program, (2) the kinds of students to be served, and (3) the specialized services which may be needed in order to implement the program. Organization may be thought of as consisting of a series of information-finding steps that are prerequisite to administration.

Administration concerns that phase of educational planning that attempts to implement the instructional program proposed by the organization process. It involves the development of policies and procedures which are designed to provide guides and rules for the conduct of the instructional program. It includes such functions as (1) scheduling of classes, (2) selection and assignment of the instructional staff, (3) class organization, and (4) the utilization of the facilities and equipment provided for the program. Its effectiveness can be determined only by how well it assists in increasing or improving the service to the student.

This chapter presents some guide lines for the organization of an adapted physical education program.

Adapted Physical Education and the Regular Program

Adapted physical education is *physical education* and not something alien or different. This statement means that the activities, equipment, and facilities provided for the regular physical education program are also used in the adapted program. In both instances, the programs must be carefully planned and directed to provide a wide variety of physical activity. All activities should be planned to improve the student's physical education. Regular and adapted physical education vary only in terms of the students for whom the programs are designed. The regular physical education program is designed to serve those students who lack physical handicaps. These students may participate in rigorous physical activity. Adapted physical education is designed for those students who may not safely participate in the activities of the regular program because of the limitations imposed by their physical divergencies.

Students assigned to adapted physical education may—and should—benefit from their participation in a program of physical activity, and their program should include many of the activities of their nonhandicapped peers. However, it is necessary that their activities be restricted or modified. The specific movement experiences or physical activities included in the regular program are selected on the basis of the interests, needs, and capacities that characterize the group. In contrast, the adapted program is based upon the individual's medical or physical limitations as well as his previous movement experiences. Thus, in essence, the adapted program is an individually prescribed program of physical activity.

Determining the Need

The initial step in the organization of an adapted physical education program is the determination of the need for such a program. This procedure involves the identification of students for possible assignment to the adapted program and it involves the determination of the types and frequency of the handicapping conditions which limit the students' physical activity.

Every school has students who are unable to participate in the regular physical education program. These students may have conditions which exempt them temporarily or permanently. In practically all instances, the handicapped students are excused from physical education altogether because the school does not provide a program of physical education that is designed to meet their special needs and interests.

In surveying the school population to determine the need for an adapted program, one must make use of all possible sources of information. Therefore, it is essential that administrative approval is secured prior to the conduct of the survey. Because of the nature of the needed information, it is essential to gain the cooperation of the personnel of the school health services.

Many school districts require periodic physical examination of all students as a condition of enrollment. Thus, the schools have records concerning the physical status of their students. A rather complete cumulative health record is maintained for each student in some school districts. Such a record is of utmost value in securing information concerning those students who may benefit from participation in the adapted program.

Other school districts do not require physical examinations nor do they maintain health records for all students. They may have records for those students who have recently had an examination in order to determine the possible existence of a physical anomaly. Unfortunately, many schools do not have any health records for students other than an informal request for exemption from physical education. This type of request is usually initiated by the student's parents or his family physician.

Regardless of the nature or extent of the health records maintained by the school, every effort should be made to gain the needed information from these records. Thus, through a review of the existing records it is possible to determine those students who may be assigned to the adapted program. Furthermore, it is possible to determine the kind and frequency of the physical handicaps of these students. Another approach that may be used in the conduct of the survey is to request the teachers to report the names of their students who are not participating in physical education. This procedure will provide a list of names which may be checked against the health records. In those schools that do not maintain any records, the task becomes more involved.

A group meeting or a personal interview with those students who have been excused from regular physical education will provide a portion of the desired information. The students should be informed about the purposes of the survey. Their cooperation should be requested in providing information concerning their physical status. It is important to emphasize the positive aspects of the survey. Therefore, it is essential to stress that the purpose of the survey is to find those handicapped students who are interested in learning new skills and increasing their knowledge of games, sports, and other physical activities which they may use for recreation in their leisure. Each should be requested to give information concerning the nature and extent of his disability and the limitations it imposes on his physical activity. Frequently, the student's knowledge, understanding, and acceptance of his disability is limited and even inaccurate. This lack of education may in itself be a justification for providing an adapted program. In order to secure complete and accurate information concerning the medical status and physical limitations, the students should be asked to identify their family physicians. The physicians may then be contacted. The necessary information may be secured by means of a checklist or questionnaire.

The results of the survey will identify those students who are not in or should not participate in the regular physical education program. It should also provide information concerning the kinds of conditions which limit or prohibit vigorous physical activity. These conditions may then be classified or grouped into various diagnoses and frequencies to reveal the physical limitations and needs of those students for whom the proposed program is to be provided. The characteristics of the students must serve as one of the bases for planning the adapted program.

Enlisting Medical Cooperation

Since adapted physical education is a program of physical activities or movement experiences for students with physical limitations, it is essential to secure adequate medical cooperation. The greatest weakness in existing adapted programs is in terms of the medical direction and supervision required.

Frequently, the school requires the teacher of adapted physical education to assume responsibilities which are beyond the scope of his training and professional authority. The teacher is requested to select students to be enrolled in the program, and on the basis of this selection he must decide the specific activities for each student. Thus, he is required to determine the physical status of the students. On the basis of his evaluation or examination, he is forced to determine the nature and extent of the individual's apparent deviation from the norm. Those students who, in his opinion, deviate markedly from the norm are assigned by the physical educator to the adapted program. The teacher must also determine those motor activities, exercises, games and sports that he feels will ameliorate the student's condition.

Although the physical educator is trained to observe marked adaptations of posture and movement as well as the demands and benefits of various forms of physical activity, only the physician is professionally and legally qualified to determine the cause and implications of the individual's adaptations. The teacher should refer those students to a physician, who, in his opinion, vary from the norm to such an extent that it is questionable whether they may participate safely or successfully in the regular physical education program. The physician then determines the nature and extent of the student's disability and the limitation or implication of his condition upon his participation in physical activity. It is the physican's diagnosis and his recommendation that provide the basis for a sound program of adapted physical education.

The physical educator must assume the initiative for securing the needed medical supervision. The family physician frequently is not well informed concerning the physical education programs of the schools. Therefore, the practice of submitting a lengthy list of physical education activities and requesting the physician to check those in which the student may participate is very questionable. The physician's recommendations are only as valid or as good as his knowledge of the various activities.

Medical doctors often write a broad or general exemption from all physical education. The first step in preventing this situation is to provide a method of informing physicians about the activities to be included in the proposed program. This information should include some indication of the intensity of the physical demands in the various activities. In addition, the physicians should be informed about the nature and purposes of the proposed program of adapted physical education. The properly prepared physical educator is qualified to describe and interpret the kinesiophysiological demands of activity as well as the degree of competition which is included in the program. Such information will assist the physician in making his specific recommendations concerning the physical education of the student.

The physician is often not aware of the training or the interest of those physical educators who are conducting the special classes for students who are not well skilled or who are physically handicapped. Furthermore, he is generally uninformed concerning the existing physical education classes provided for the physically handicapped students. He often believes that the program is rigidly structured and that specific recommendations or requests from him concerning a student patient are beyond the limit or scope of the program. It is imperative that the school administrator convey to him that the adapted program is the school's attempt to provide the handicapped child with a physical education program which will benefit the child. The administration should inform the physician that the instructor is qualified to conduct and supervise the activities included in a good program of adapted physical education. Last, emphasis must be placed on the need for the physician's cooperation. His cooperation is basic to insuring that his student patient receives the maximum benefits from participation in the activities of the adapted program.

The physical educator and the school cannot secure the cooperation of the private physician alone, but must—in some degree at least—incorporate as well the efforts of the school nurse, school physician, or consultant physician. Securing the private physician's cooperation is not an attempt to minimize the valuable assistance of school health personnel, which is needed in planning or organizing the proposed program. It is, however, an attempt to point out that after medical assistance in developing the program has been completed, the school health personnel must provide the guidance and responsibility for informing their colleagues about the adapted program.

In those instances in which the school provides a school physician, his cooperation is essential to the organization of a sound adapted program. He should be requested to assist in the formulation of the policies and procedures concerning the selection and assignment of students to adapted physical education. These should include policies and procedures concerning the responsibility for the determination or diagnosis of the student's physical status. He should help determine whether the examination is to be conducted by him or his associates or by the student's private physician. A policy clearly indicating his responsibility for the assignment of students to the program as well as a procedure for handling recommendations for activity should be developed. His guidance should also be requested for the kinds of activities and specific exercises which may be used in the physical education of students with various physical limitations, conditions, or handicaps. The sports, games, and exercise routines to be included in the adapted program should be developed by the physical educator and approved by the school physician. Or better, the physician and physical educator may design a program together. Thus, the school physician assumes a second major responsibility for the adapted program. He assists in providing the needed medical guidance in the selection of the activities to be included in the physical education of physically handicapped students.

In those instances where there is no specifically designated school physician, the problem of securing medical direction and supervision of adapted physical education is more difficult. Fortunately, many of the schools do provide a school nurse. Although the nurse cannot provide the needed medical guidance for the program, she is often able to assist in providing the initial contact with the physicians in the community. If neither a school physician nor a school nurse is provided, the physical educator must assume the responsibility for contacting local physicians to secure a physician who is willing to serve as a consultant for the adapted program. The physician will have to volunteer his service gratis in most instances.

Another approach to securing the needed medical direction is to contact the various medical associations and health departments at the local, county, and state levels. They frequently have established procedures for providing their services to the schools. Regardless of the manner in which the needed guidance is provided, the individual physician should be one who is vitally interested in physical education. In addition to his being willing to assist in planning the adapted program, he must also be willing to assist in informing and gaining the cooperation of the other physicians within the community.

Classifying the Student's Physical Status

It is the physician's diagnosis and his recommendation concerning the student's activity program that serves as the basis for adapted physical education. Once the prescribing physician has been informed of the purpose of the program, it is essential to provide some method by which the medical or physical status of the student may be classified or grouped. The specific diagnosis of the student's condition is important to the teacher. The need for the physician's recommendations concerning the nature of the limitations which his diagnosis imposes upon the student's physical activity program is of utmost importance. A classification code must be developed and utilized by the physician which will provide the physical educator with the basic information that is necessary to plan and direct an adapted program.

The development of a classification code which would indicate the specific limitations imposed by every kind of physical divergency would be of little value, because it would be too involved and too lengthy for practical application. Therefore, the medical classification code for physical education should consist of generalized limitations or contraindications which could be imposed by any one of several different physical divergencies. The determination of the classification code categories should be based upon careful analysis of the various physical divergencies. Similarity of specific limitations imposed by each kind of divergency could provide a basis upon which categories could be formed. Thus, it is the nature of the student's physical-activity limitation which serves as the basis for planning his individual program. Such categories might include one that would indicate that the individual should limit his energy output; another category would indicate that the individual should not participate in any activity which could by its nature expose the individual to trauma; another category would be that in which the individual is to avoid those activities that would result in increasing his intra-abdominal pressure. However, the use of a classification code should not limit the physician's recommendations concerning the individual's activity program. Rather, it should encourage him to make specific suggestions concerning exercises that should be included in the student's program. These suggestions should be made to ameliorate the student's physical handicap.

Nature and Scope of the Program

Any educational program is influenced by the kinds of students for whom it is designed as well as by the purposes for which it is intended. The nature and scope of an adapted program will be greatly influenced by the philosophy of the physical education department, the nature and the extent of the needs of the students assigned to the program, and the physician's diagnosis and recommendation. Therefore, it is of questionable value to list specific games, sports, and rhythms that might be included in the program. The requirement of specific equipment and facilities which must be provided in order to offer an adapted program is also inconsistent with good educational planning. However, it is possible to make generalizations concerning what should characterize a good adapted physical education program.

The students whom the physicians might recommend for enrollment in the adapted program fall into one or more of four general groups: (1) those desiring to rehabilitate a physical disability, (2) those desiring to adapt to a permanent physical handicap, (3) those requiring a limited physical activity program, and (4) those requiring a developmental program. These generalized groups should be considered the kinds of students who will be enrolled in the program. The needs of these students will help to determine the nature and scope of the program that is to be provided. On the basis of these groups, certain implications for program planning are evident.

Although it is possible to give an indication of the nature and scope of the program based on the needs of the various groups, it must be remembered that adapted physical education is primarily an individualized program. A student may, because of the complexity of his condition, be assigned or classified into more than one of the groups in terms of his needs. Therefore, it is necessary to decide whether the sports or the therapeutic-exercise phase of the program will best meet or satisfy his needs. It is often necessary to classify his needs as either immediate or long term. His program would be planned accordingly. Even though he may receive greater benefits from participation in one phase of the program than in the other, it might be advisable to have him participate in both.

Many teachers of adapted physical education indicate that the major limiting factors which influence the nature and scope of their programs are the facilities and the equipment that are provided for use in the program. In many instances, it is not the lack of appropriate equipment or facilities, but the improper utilization of existing materials which limit the program. One problem concerning facilities and equipment for the adapted program is that they are frequently planned or selected too early in the organization process. Because of the special needs of the students, many teachers feel that the program can only be conducted in specially designed facilities. Many teachers also feel that special equipment is needed. This attitude has often resulted in delaying the program as well as unnecessarily restricting or curtailing its nature and scope. Determination of facilities and equipment to be used in the adapted program must be made only after careful consideration of the implications of the needs of the students whom it is to serve.

An adequate program of adapted physical education may be provided by any school that offers a regular physical education program. It is *not* necessary to have special activities, equipment, and facilities prior to offering an adapted program. An adequate adapted physical education program can be offered immediately through the utilization of carefully selected, and in some instances modified, activities, facilities, and equipment of the existing regular physical education program.

The program does, however, require certain facilities and equipment to satisfy some specific requirements. Provision should be made for an indoor area or room which may serve as an exercise center. Games and sports areas are also needed. It is advisable to have both indoor and outdoor facilities for those phases of the program. The facilities and equipment which are to be used in the program may, for the most part, be those which are also used in the regular physical education program. The major problem is not the unavailability of needed instructional materials and areas, but the failure effectively to incorporate existing facilities and equipment of the regular program into the adapted program.

In conclusion, the organization process for adapted physical education is primarily concerned with securing medical direction and supervision which will serve as the basis for program planning. Through the utilization of the physician's diagnosis and recommendation, the student's needs, and the philosophy of the physical education department a program of physical activity or of movement experiences may be provided for those students whose physical condition prohibits or limits their participation in the regular physical education program.

Selected References

AAHPER Committee on Adapted Physical Education, "Guiding Principles for Adapted Physical Education," *The Journal of the American Association for Health, Physical Education and Recreation*, XXIII, No. 4 (April 1952), 15, 18.

Clarke, H. Harrison, and David H. Clarke, *Developmental and Adapted Physical Education*. Englewood Cliffs, N.J.: Prentice-Hall, Inc., 1963.

Daniels, Arthur S., *Adapted Physical Education*. New York: Harper & Row, Publishers, 1954.

Howland, Ivalclare Sprow, *Adapted Physical Education in Schools*. Dubuque, Iowa: Wm. C. Brown Co., 1959.

Mathews, Donald K., Robert Kruse, and Virginia Shaw, *The Science of Physical Education for Handicapped Children*. New York: Harper & Row, Publishers, 1962.

15

ADMINISTRATION OF THE ADAPTED PROGRAM

Although program planning, organization, and administration are often treated synonymously, differences exist which must receive consideration. The organization phase of program planning is functionally defined in Chapter 14 as: "an attempt to discover and answer questions concerning the nature and scope of the proposed program." It is in terms of this function of finding information that the organization process provides the basis for and is prerequisite to the implementation and conduct of the program. Consequently, through the use of the organization process, the need arises for the development of a policy as the basis for the establishment of procedures for the conduct of the proposed program.

Administration is that phase of educational planning which is concerned with the development and the utilization of policies and procedures for the implementation and conduct of the instructional program. Thus, an evaluation of the instructional program will be greatly influenced by the nature of those practices which serve as the bases for the conduct of the program. Therefore, the final determination of the effectiveness of educational planning is based on the answer to the question: "How well and to what extent do the adopted policies and procedures assist the student in achieving the objectives of the program?"

For those readers who are planning to teach at the secondary school level, it is appropriate here to discuss those aspects of administrative planning which are common to adapted physical education programs at the junior and senior high school levels. It is beyond the scope of this book or any book to discuss specific administrative practices for all school situations. There are general principles that should serve as guides to the administration and conduct of any adapted physical education program. Therefore, it must be remembered that the specific practices and administrative forms discussed here are to be considered applications of a principle or policy. These practices should be evaluated, accepted, or rejected in terms of the local situation.

THE ADMINISTRATIVE HANDBOOK

It is imperative that specific policies and procedures be developed and utilized in order to help the adapted physical education program function efficiently and effectively. The collection and incorporation of these policies and procedures into an organized and written form results in the evolution of an administrative handbook.

The purpose of such a handbook is to outline the policy as the basis for the establishment of procedures utilized in the conduct of the program. In view of its purpose, the handbook may serve as (1) an operational guide in administering the program; (2) a reference for the application of policy concerning the cooperation or coordination of the school health services, the student's personal physician, and the department of physical education; (3) a resource guide in the administration of the physical education department with regard to the adapted physical education program, facilities, equipment, staff, intra- and interdepartmental relationships; and (4) a reference in maintaining continuity and consistency in regard to policies and procedures within the adapted physical education program.

THE ADMINISTRATIVE PROCESS

The administrative process is an attempt to develop policies and procedures which will implement the proposed program through the organization process. The effectiveness of the process and the justification of the specific practices must be determined only in terms of how well it assists in increasing or improving the service to the student.

The planning of any educational program must be predicated upon a sound philosophy. Objectives of the program that provide the basis for administrative practice must be consistent with the philosophy. For example, the belief that adapted physical education must have its basis in the physician's diagnosis and recommendation requires the acceptance of the principle that there must be cooperation between the physician and the adapted physical education staff. In order to implement this principle, administrative policy and procedures must be established that will clearly define the relationship and the responsibilities of the medical and instructional staff concerning such problem areas as (1) medical classification of students for physical education, (2) assignment of students to the adapted program, (3) referral to the physician, and (4) reassignment of students in adapted physical education to the regular physical education program.

A further illustration of the application of the administrative process is the problem of medical classification of students for physical education. There are numerous methods by which the physician may indicate the limitations which he feels must guide the physical education experiences of his student patient. One of these methods requires the physician to indicate the specific physical education activities in which the student may participate. There may be games such as handball, badminton, table tennis, and volleyball. Another method requires the physician to indicate the degree of physical exertion which the student may safely expend while participating in physical activity. These degrees are usually indicated as mild, moderate, regular, or severe exertion. However, in both of these methods, the physician's recommendations are only as valid as his knowledge of the energy requirements for participation in the activities is accurate. Therefore, a method which permits the physician to indicate the required or requested limitations of the student's activity based on his knowledge of the student's physical condition and its implications is necessary.

In view of the previous discussion, the following procedure, or a similar one, is recommended as a guide for adapted physical education programming: (1) before engaging in any activity within the physical education program, all students must have their physical status certified by their personal physicians or by the school physician; (2) as a phase of the physical examination, the student's medical status must be classified in relation to his participation in the physical education program; (3) the examining physician shall complete a medical classification card for each student whose physical condition makes restriction or special supervision of his physical activities desirable; and (4) the physical education department shall keep the medical classification cards on file for all students currently enrolled in physical education.

Medical Classification System

A desirable method of classifying the medical status of students is one that permits the physician to communicate to the adapted physical education staff broad, general recommendations for the student. Such a method should convey not only the contraindications—those things which should be avoided in programming the student's physical education—but should also give additional information concerning the nature of the program that will best meet the needs of the student. A simple recommended coding system which involves the use of letters and numbers is the "UCLA system." This coding system, reported by Lorenzo J. Rossi, Jr.,[1] provides an excellent guide for adapted physical education programming.

At the time of the physical examination, each student is classified into one of three main groups, "A," "B," or "C." Each student is issued a medical classification card (Fig. 15.1).[2] Those students

---

[1] "Corrective Therapy in a School Environment," *Journal of the Association for Physical and Mental Rehabilitation,* VIII, No. 4 (July-August 1954), 115–116.

[2] Figures 15.1, 15.2, and 15.3 are reproduced here by permission of the Department of Physical Education, University of California, Los Angeles.

UNIVERSITY OF CALIFORNIA, LOS ANGELES
Department of Physical Education
MEDICAL CLASSIFICATION CARD

name   last   first

has been classified
by the University
Physician

A

date   signed

NO RESTRICTIONS

10m-10,'60(B4425s4)6493

UNIVERSITY OF CALIFORNIA, LOS ANGELES
Department of Physical Education
MEDICAL CLASSIFICATION CARD

name   last   first

has been classified
by the University
Physician

B

date   signed

NO SWIMMING

15m-7,'54(5726s4)6493

UNIVERSITY OF CALIFORNIA, LOS ANGELES
Department of Physical Education
MEDICAL CLASSIFICATION CARD

name   last   first

has been classified
by the University
Physician

C

date   signed

10m-7,'54(5726s4)6493

Figure 15.1

who are classified "C" require a restricted program or require
special supervision of their physical activity, and the physician indicates the nature of the limitation as well as the nature of the
program which will best meet the student's needs by using the
appropriate number or numbers listed in the following code:

"A"—Not Restricted.

"B"—No Swimming (sinusitis, allergy, ear infection, etc.).

"C"—Special or Restricted. (Student is to be placed under the supervision of the adapted physical education staff.)

(1) *Energy Output to Be Kept Down:* Should avoid dyspnea and fatigue. Cases of heart disease, asthma, convalescence from infectious disease, etc., will fall under this classification. Specify degree of restriction.

(2) *Protect from Trauma:* Students with atrophied limbs, recent fractures, cerebral concussions, high myopia, front teeth recently straightened, etc.[3]

(3) *No Close Contact with Other Students or with Mats; Keep out of Pool:* Cases of repulsive or mildly infectious skin disease, such as pustular acne, psoriasis, or eczema are in this category.

(4) *Not to Use Legs More than Necessary:* Students, otherwise normal, who suffer from mild foot strain, old leg injuries, healed thrombophlebitis, etc.

(5) *Keep out of Pool and off High Places:* Persons subject to convulsive seizures or periods of disturbed consciousness.

(6) *Adapt Activity to Some Deformity:* For students who are blind or deaf or have lost a limb, but who are not particularly fragile; and similar cases.

(7) *Avoid Increased Intra-Abdominal Pressure:* Such as caused by heavy lifting or straining. For students with hernia. (Recent appendectomy, or other abdominal surgery.)

(8) *Recommended for Certain Regular Physical Education Classes (Activities):* To be used when the physician wishes to specify certain regular physical education activity which would be beneficial, such as swimming, for patients with muscle weakness following poliomyelitis.

(9) *Recommended for Special Corrective Physical Exercises:* For students who do not need to have their activity limited but who would benefit in a positive way from special exercises designed to correct or alleviate some defective condition. Pronated feet, recurrent shoulder dislocations,

---

[3] Although those students with myopia and teeth difficulties are to be protected from trauma, it has proven satisfactory to have instead a fourth classification, "C2," for these students. The prescribing physician notes whether the classification is for myopia or teeth. The major contraindication is to keep these students from physical contact sports, particularly if they wear glasses.

muscular under-development, some cases of dysmenorrhea, and unusually poor posture are a few examples.

(10) (0) *No Physical Education:* If the University requirement in physical education is to remain unfulfilled because of physical defect, the approval of the Director or Assistant Director of the Student Health Service is required, on the special yellow exemption form provided by the Registrar's Office.

Medical Recommendation Card

With the adoption of a medical classification system, it becomes necessary to develop a form upon which the physician may indicate his recommendations. An example of such a form, previously referred to as a medical classification card, is shown in Figure 15.2. The card provides space for the physician to indicate the diagnosis of the student's condition. In addition, the physician should use the appropriate space to list specific recommendations concerning the student's physical education program.

Medical Examination Record and Recommendations, Student Health Service

Name.. Class.................... Date....................
         PRINT last name first   Numerals

Present Height............ Present Weight............ Age............ Admitted to Upper Division....................

Medical Classification (Circle One)	C_2	Myopia................	Space Reserved for Dept. of Physical Education
A No Restriction		Teeth................	
B No swimming			
C Special— 1 2 3 4 5 6 7 8 9 0		Temp. Perm.	Strict Mild

Nature of Disability:..

Special Recommendations:..

....

.... Signed....................................
                                    University Physician

5m-5,'61(B9547s2)777   UNIVERSITY OF CALIFORNIA, LOS ANGELES
                                      DEPARTMENT OF PHYSICAL EDUCATION

Figure 15.2

Posture Examination Record

The development and utilization of a form for the recording of significant findings of individual posture screening is desirable. This form may be used by the physician when conducting the postural or orthopedic aspects of the physical examination. The instructor of adapted physical education may also use the form when conducting preliminary posture screening of students for possible referral to a physician. By the use of different colored inks or pencils, a single form may be used for recording periodic rechecks in order to indicate the degree of amelioration or correction which may have occurred. An example of such a form is shown in Figure 15.3. The extent or severity of each of the possible deviations may be checked by use of the numbers, "1," "2," or "3." There are no set criteria for the use of these numbers in terms of severity of the divergencies, but the following or similar standards may be used: (1) *noticeable or slight,* approximately ½-inch deviation; (2) *mild or moderate,* approximately 1 to 1½ inches deviation; (3) *severe,* more than 1½ or 2 inches deviation.

Medical Referral Procedure

Ideally, each student enrolled in physical education would have a physical examination and a medical classification yearly. But this practice is seldom encountered; physical examinations are usually scheduled only when the student enters the first grade, seventh grade, and high school. However, there are many instances when the student needs medical reclassification. Some may require reclassification as a result of an injury received in the vigorous activity classes of the regular physical education program, intramurals, and the interscholastic program. Others may require reevaluation of their classification in relation to the activity in which they are currently enrolled or participating. Finally, some may need reclassification because of a change in their medical status as a result of illness, disease, or operation, or as a consequence of their response to participation in rehabilitation activities of the adapted program.

Regardless of the reason for the medical reclassification of his

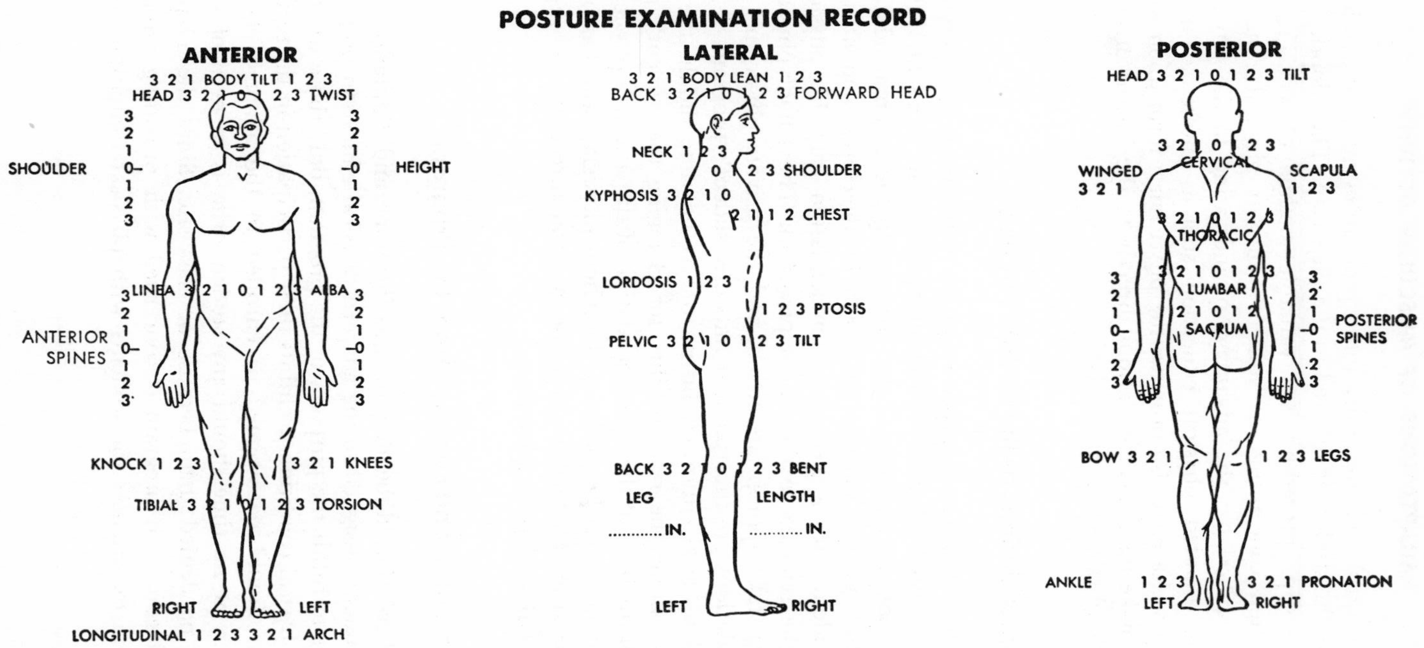

POSTURE EXAMINATION RECORD

ANTERIOR

3 2 1 BODY TILT 1 2 3 TWIST
HEAD 3 2 1 0 1 2 3

HEIGHT

3
2
1
0
1
2
3

SHOULDER

3 LINEA 3 2 1 0 1 2 3 ALBA 3
2
1
0
1
2
3

ANTERIOR
SPINES

3 2 1 KNEES
KNOCK 3 2 1 0 1 2 3
TIBIAL 3 2 1 0 1 2 3 TORSION

RIGHT   LEFT
LONGITUDINAL 1 2 3 3 2 1 ARCH

LATERAL

3 2 1 BODY LEAN 1 2 3
BACK 3 2 1 0 1 2 3 FORWARD HEAD

NECK 1 2 3
SHOULDER 3 2 1 0 1 2 3
CHEST 3 2 1 0 1 2 3
KYPHOSIS 3 2 1 0
PTOSIS 3 2 1 0 1 2 3
LORDOSIS 1 2 3
PELVIC 3 2 1 0 1 2 3 TILT

BACK 3 2 1 0 1 2 3 BENT

LENGTH
LEG .... IN. .... IN.

LEFT   RIGHT

Figure 15.3

POSTERIOR

HEAD 3 2 1 0 1 2 3 TILT

SCAPULA 1 2 3
CERVICAL 3 2 1 0 1 2 3
WINGED 3 2 1
THORACIC 3 2 1 0 1 2 3
POSTERIOR SPINES 3 2 1 0 1 2 3
LUMBAR 3 2 1 0 1 2 3
SACRUM 3 2 1 0 1 2 3

BOW 3 2 1
LEGS 1 2 3

ANKLE   RIGHT 3 2 1 PRONATION
LEFT 1 2 3

physical status, definite policies and procedures must be developed whereby the student is referred to the physician. The adoption of a "referral slip" procedure is a valuable method of securing new information concerning the student's current physical condition. Such a method has the advantage of indicating to the physician that the adapted physical education staff is interested in the student's welfare. It also provides the physician a form upon which he can make his recommendations directly to the instructor of the student's physical education class.

Recommendations of the Private Physician

Where the school physician provides the medical supervision of the adapted physical education program, it is essential that definite policies and procedures concerning the recommendations from the student's personal physician be developed and utilized. The student with a medical recommendation from his physician should be referred to the school physician. The school physician will then take appropriate action, and the private physician's recommendations are incorporated into the student's program by the adapted physical education instructor. At no time should the instructor assume the responsibility for changing the student's program on the basis of the recommendation of the student's physician. Such changes must be made by the school physician who has been delegated the responsibility for the medical direction and supervision of the adapted program.

Assignment to and Removal from the Program

There should be definite qualifications and limitations for those students assigned to the adapted physical education program. In order to fulfill the purposes of the program, only those students whose physical condition prohibits their participation in the regular program should be assigned or enrolled in the adapted classes. However, at no time should any student who is in need of such services be denied them because of class size. Since the adapted physical education program is concerned with providing physical education experiences for students with physical limitations, it is essential that a physician certify the student's medical status before the student is considered for assignment to the program.

There should be definite policies and procedures established for the assignment of students to adapted physical education. There should also be policies and procedures for their reassignment to the regular physical education program. Such assignment or reassignment may be determined by the receipt of the medical classification and recommendation card by the instructor of the specific class. However, since the assignment of a student to adapted physical education may involve major changes in his total school program, it may be more advantageous to establish an *admissions* and *dismissal committee*. This committee should consist of (1) the school physician, (2) the school nurse, (3) the instructor of adapted physical education, (4) the school guidance counselor, and (5) the administrative officer of the school.

If one accepts the belief that the aim of the adapted physical education program is to return the student to regular physical education, it is essential that the student be encouraged to participate in selected activities of the regular physical education program following a satisfactory rehabilitation period. If the student's condition permits him to participate safely and successfully in the selected activities, he should then be encouraged to return to the regular physical education program. In order to implement this belief, there should be periodic reevaluations of each student enrolled in these classes. In particular, this reevaluation should be made prior to enrollment in or assignment to physical education for the following semester. Reevaluation should be made by both the teacher and the prescribing physician.

Temporary Restrictions

Because of the nature of the activities included in the regular physical education program, it is not unusual for students to receive various kinds of joint injuries. The majority of these injuries are sprains or strains which do not require extensive periods of time for recuperation. However, they may prohibit the student's participation from a day to three or four weeks. In addition, during the school year, several students may be expected to receive more serious injuries. Conditions to be expected are (1) fractures or dislocations, (2) serious illness involving long periods of convalescence, and (3) postsurgery rehabilitation. It is obvious that individuals with these conditions must not participate in vigorous physical activity for an indefinite period of time. Therefore, it is essential to develop policies and procedures for those students who have temporary restrictions of their participation in the regular physical education program.

The following or similar procedures are recommended for handling temporary restrictions:

1. When the student's disability is such that it is expected to limit or restrict his participation in the regular program for a semester or more, the student should be sent to the school physician or his personal physician so that his medical classification may be reclassified. The prescribing physician should include on the medical recommendation card the diagnosis, classification, recommendation, and the expected period for which the restriction is to apply. The student is then assigned to the adapted program. At the termination of the semester or of the period of time for the restriction, the instructor should send the student to the prescribing physician for reevaluation. This procedure will generally result in the reclassification of the student's medical status and the resultant reassignment to the regular physical education program.

2. When the student's disability is expected to limit or restrict his participation in the regular program for more than a week, the instructor of the regular physical education class should send the student to the instructor of the adapted physical education program. At this time, in conference with the student and depending upon the reason for restriction, the decision will be made whether or not the student should be referred to the prescribing physician for possible reclassification. Whether or not the student is referred to the physician, he should keep up his attendance and participation in some desirable activity in the adapted program. If the student was sent to the physician for examination, he should be automatically reclassified by the adapted physical education staff at the end of the restriction period. This procedure would be followed unless the physician indicated that he would like to see the student again. Therefore, it is advisable for the prescribing physician to indicate on the medical recommendation card if the student is to be automatically reclassified at the end of the time for the restric-

tion, or whether he wants to reevaluate the student's condition prior to reclassification. However, the instructor should never reclassify the student at the end of the restriction period unless he is sure that the student is able to participate in the regular program safely and successfully. Under no circumstances should he reclassify any student who evidences any complications of his original condition.

3. When the student's disability is such that it is expected to limit his participation in the regular physical education program for less than a week, the student's physical activity usually may be adjusted quite satisfactorily by the regular class instructor. The instructor may limit the individual's participation, permit him to attend class without actually participating, or modify his class participation in some other appropriate manner. However, when the instructor is in doubt as to what he should do concerning the student, he should send the student to the instructor of the adapted program for advisement and possible program modification.

Scheduling Classes

The scheduling of adapted physical education classes should be predicated upon the principle of serving the students most efficiently and effectively. Ideally, there should be an adapted class whenever there is a regular physical education class scheduled. This coordination would facilitate the interclass transfer of students from the regular program to the adapted program. Ease of transfer is very important for students injured in the regular program as well as for students who are ill for periods ranging from a week to a month. However, since it is impossible or even unnecessary to schedule that many classes in most schools, careful planning must guide the scheduling of the adapted classes. If the school has an interscholastic program that holds its team practices during the last period of the school day, it is recommended that an adapted class be scheduled also during that period to permit those student athletes who are injured in the interscholastic program to receive guidance and supervision to facilitate the rehabilitation of their injuries. This scheduling will not necessitate any major changes in the school program and the athletes will be able to benefit from the adapted program.

Programming Students

In order to provide an adapted physical education program which includes both a therapeutic-exercise phase and a sports phase, adequate supervision must be assured. One of the major problems in programming adapted physical education concerns the way in which the teacher may supervise both phases of the program at the same time. There is little question that the student may benefit from participating in both phases of the program. Therefore, it is suggested that the program be organized so that both phases are provided for each class. This may be accomplished by scheduling the therapeutic exercise phase on Monday, Wednesday, and Friday and the sports phase on Tuesday and Thursday.

Another method might involve the scheduling of each phase of the program for a period of time during each semester. For example, the therapeutic-exercise phase may be scheduled for the first half of the semester with the sports phase scheduled during the last half. If there is a sufficient number of students assigned to the program, it may be possible to schedule separate classes of therapeutic exercise and sports. However, it is strongly recommended that in such an arrangement the assignments be flexible in order to permit transfer from one class or phase to another.

For those students whose conditions permit, provision must be made for their participation in the selected activities within the regular physical education program. For example, a student may be assigned to regular physical education for badminton instruction. At the termination of the instructional period of the activity, the student is reassigned or returned to the adapted program. This procedure of assigning students on a limited basis to a regular physical education class is referred to as a "farm-out." In implementing the farm-out procedure, a close liaison is imperative between the teacher in the adapted program and the teacher in the regular physical education program to whose class the student is assigned.

In order to meet effectively the needs of the students assigned to adapted physical education, there must be periodic individual and group conferences between the students and the instructor. It is recommended that group and individual conferences be held during the first two or three meetings of the class.

The purpose of the initial group meeting is to orient all the students to the adapted program. This orientation should include departmental rules and regulations, purpose and objectives of the adapted program, and its nature and scope. The latter would include a discussion of the therapeutic-exercise and sports phases of the program.

The small group discussions and the individual conferences are utilized to help each student set up his program. This assistance is basic to the hope of achieving the objectives of the program. The discussions and conferences are also concerned with determining the specific areas and exercises to be used for the rehabilitation or general conditioning of those students assigned to the therapeutic-exercise phase of the program. They also assist in the selection of specific sports, games, and rhythms to be used by those students assigned to the sports phase of the program.

Following the discussions and conferences, the students are given instruction concerning their particular program of exercises or sport activities in which they will participate. Again, because of the commonality of limitations of activity and medical recommendations for various kinds of handicapping conditions, it is more efficient in terms of time to group the students by commonalities for the purposes of instruction and supervision. It was on the basis of commonalities that the "exercise routine" concept discussed in Chapter 12 was developed for use in administering exercises for most joint disabilities. The student assigned to the therapeutic-exercise phase of the program, after having received instruction and learned his specific program, should be instructed to record his progress on work cards.

The students who are assigned to the sports phase of the program should be encouraged to participate in individual or dual activities such as badminton, table tennis, paddle tennis, or other activities within their capabilities and limitations. In addition, they should be encouraged to participate in group or team activities such as volleyball, softball, and basketball according to the criteria for selection of group, team, activities individual, and dual activities discussed in Chapter 13.

In Conclusion

The task of the teacher of adapted physical education is to plan and direct a program of physical activities for those students who are unable to participate safely or successfully in the regular physical education program. In fulfilling his responsibilities, he must be guided by the medical diagnosis and recommendation of the physician. In planning the program, the teacher must utilize his knowledge of (1) the limitations of the student's condition; (2) the biophysiological characteristics of man; (3) the physiological demands of the various games, sports, rhythms, and aquatic activities; and (4) the principles of exercise. In this way, the teacher selects those physical activities which will aid in the amelioration, elimination, or reversal of those adaptations which are imposed by the force of gravity, trauma, congenital anomaly, or pathological divergency.

Selected References

Corrective Physical Education: Teaching Guide for Junior and Senior High Schools. Los Angeles City Schools, Division of Instructional Services, Pub. No. SC-566.

Fait, Hollis F., *Adapted Physical Education.* Philadelphia: W. B. Saunders Co., 1960.

Lowman, Charles LeRoy, and Carl Haven Young, *Postural Fitness: Significance and Variances.* Philadelphia: Lea & Febiger, 1960.

Stafford, George T., and Ellen Davis Kelly, *Preventive and Corrective Physical Education,* 3rd ed. New York: Ronald Press Co., 1958.

APPENDIX

Selected Books and Periodicals

Books

Anastasi, Anne, *Differential Psychology*. New York: Macmillan Co., 1962.

Billig, Harvey E., Jr., and Evelyn Lowendahl, *Mobilization of the Human Body*. Stanford, Calif.: Stanford University Press, 1949.

Breckenridge, Marian E., and E. Lee Vincent, *Child Development*, 4th ed. Philadelphia: W. B. Saunders Co., 1960.

Clarke, H. Harrison, and David H. Clarke, *Developmental and Adapted Physical Education*. Englewood Cliffs, N.J.: Prentice-Hall, Inc., 1963.

Daniels, Arthur S., *Adapted Physical Education*. New York: Harper & Row, Publishers, 1954.

Davies, Evelyn A., *The Elementary School Child and His Posture Patterns*. New York: Appleton-Century-Crofts, Inc., 1958.

Davis, Elwood C., and Gene A. Logan, *Biophysical Values of Muscular Activity*. Dubuque, Iowa: Wm. C. Brown Company, 1961.

DeLorme, Thomas L., and Arthur L. Watkins, *Progressive Resistance Exercise*. New York: Appleton-Century-Crofts, Inc., 1951.

Drew, Lillian C., and Hazel L. Kinzly, *Individual Gymnastics*. Philadelphia: Lea & Febiger, 1949.

Fait, Hollis F., *Adapted Physical Education*. Philadelphia: W. B. Saunders Co., 1960.

Foote, Doreen, *Modified Activities in Physical Education*. New York: Inor Publishing Co., Inc., 1945.

Gallagher, J. Roswell, *Medical Care of the Adolescent*. New York: Appleton-Century-Crofts, Inc., 1960.

Gardiner, M. Dena, *The Principles of Exercise Therapy*. New York: Macmillan Co., 1957.

Garrison, Karl C., *Growth and Development,* 2nd ed. New York: David McKay Co., Inc., 1959.

Hettinger, Theodor, *Physiology of Strength.* Springfield, Ill.: Charles C Thomas, 1961.

Howland, Ivalclare Sprow, *Adapted Physical Education in Schools.* Dubuque, Iowa: Wm. C. Brown Co., 1959.

Huddleston, O. Leonard, *Therapeutic Exercise, Kinesiotherapy.* Philadelphia: F. A. Davis Co., 1961.

Hunt, Valerie V., *Recreation for the Handicapped.* Englewood Cliffs, N.J.: Prentice-Hall, Inc., 1955.

Hurlock, Elizabeth B., *Adolescent Development,* rev. ed. New York: Appleton-Century-Crofts, Inc., 1956.

Jacobson, Edmund, *Progressive Relaxation.* Chicago: University of Chicago Press, 1938.

——, *You Must Relax.* New York: McGraw-Hill Book Co., Inc., 1957.

Johnson, Warren R., ed., *Science and Medicine of Exercise and Sports.* New York: Harper & Row, Publishers, 1960.

Kelly, Ellen Davis, *Teaching Posture and Body Mechanics.* New York: A. S. Barnes & Co., 1949.

Kendall, Henry, and Otis Kendall, *Posture and Pain.* Baltimore: Williams & Wilkins Co., 1952.

Kraus, Hans, *Principles and Practice of Therapeutic Exercise.* Springfield, Ill.: Charles C Thomas, 1949.

Lace, Mary V., *Massage and Medical Gymnastics.* London: J. & A. Churchill, Ltd., 1946.

Lee, J. Murray, and Dorris May Lee, *The Child and His Development.* New York: Appleton-Century-Crofts, Inc., 1958.

Licht, Sidney, ed., *Therapeutic Exercise,* 2nd ed. New Haven, Conn.: Elizabeth Licht, 1961.

Logan, Gene A., et al., *Student Handbook for Adapted Physical Education.* Dubuque, Iowa: Wm. C. Brown Co., 1960.

Lowman, Charles LeRoy, et al., *Corrective Physical Education for Groups.* New York: A. S. Barnes & Co., 1928.

Lowman, Charles LeRoy, and Carl Haven Young, *Postural Fitness: Significance and Variances.* Philadelphia: Lea & Febiger, 1960.

Mathews, Donald K., Robert D. Kruse, and Virginia L. Shaw, *The Science of Physical Education for Handicapped Children.* New York: Harper & Row, Publishers, 1962.

Metheny, Eleanor, *Body Dynamics.* New York: McGraw-Hill Book Co., Inc., 1952.

Morgan, R. E., and G. T. Adamson, *Circuit Training,* rev. ed. New Rochelle, N.Y.: Sportshelf & Soccer Associates, 1962.

Morrison, Whitelaw Reid, and Laurence B. Chenoweth, *Normal and Elementary Physical Diagnosis,* 5th ed. Philadelphia: Lea & Febiger, 1955.

Rathbone, Josephine L., *Corrective Physical Education,* 6th ed. Philadelphia: W. B. Saunders Co., 1959.

——, *Teach Yourself to Relax.* Englewood Cliffs, N.J.: Prentice-Hall, Inc., 1957.

Smith, Olive F. Guthrie, *Rehabilitation, Re-education, and Remedial Exercises.* London: Bailliere, Tindall & Cox Limited, 1949.

Stafford, George T., *Sports for the Handicapped,* 2nd ed. Englewood Cliffs, N.J.: Prentice-Hall, Inc., 1947.

——, and Ellen Davis Kelly, *Preventive and Corrective Physical Education,* 3rd ed. New York: Ronald Press Co., 1958.

Stone, Eleanor B., and John W. Deyton, *Corrective Therapy for the Handicapped Child.* Englewood Cliffs, N.J.: Prentice-Hall, Inc., 1951.

Thompson, George G., *Child Psychology.* Boston: Houghton Mifflin Co., 1962.

Wallis, Earl L., and Gene A. Logan, *Figure Improvement and Body Conditioning through Exercise.* Englewood Cliffs, N.J.: Prentice-Hall, Inc., 1964.

Wiles, Philip, *Essentials of Orthopaedics,* 3rd ed. Boston: Little, Brown and Co., 1959.

Periodicals

American Journal of Diseases of Children. 535 N. Dearborn St., Chicago 10, Illinois.

American Journal of Hygiene. Johns Hopkins Press, Baltimore 18, Maryland.

American Journal of Nursing. 10 Columbus Circle, New York 19, N.Y.

American Journal of Occupational Therapy. 3514 N. Oakland Ave., Milwaukee 11, Wisconsin.

American Journal of Ophthalmology. 664 N. Michigan Ave., Chicago 11, Illinois.

American Journal of Orthopedics. 1700 Holcombe Blvd., Houston 25, Texas.

American Journal of Physical Medicine. 428 E. Preston St., Baltimore 2, Maryland.

American Journal of Physiology. 9650 Wisconsin Ave., Washington 14, D.C.

American Journal of Public Health and the Nation's Health. 1790 Broadway, New York 19, N.Y.

American Medical Association Journal. 535 N. Dearborn St., Chicago 10, Illinois.

American Physical Therapy Association Journal. 1790 Broadway, New York 19, N.Y.

Annals of Physical Medicine. 109 Kingsway, London W.C. 2, England.

Archives of Diseases in Childhood. B.M.A. House, Tavistock Square, London W.C. 1, England.

Archives of Ophthalmology. 535 N. Dearborn St., Chicago 10, Illinois.

Archives of Physical Medicine and Rehabilitation. 30 N. Michigan Ave., Chicago 2, Illinois.

Cerebral Palsy Review. 2400 Jardine Dr., Wichita 19, Kansas.

Child Development. Child Development Publications, Purdue University, Lafayette, Indiana.

Children. Children's Bureau, Supt. of Documents, Washington 25, D.C.

Exceptional Children. 1201 Sixteenth St., N.W., Washington 6, D.C.

Journal of Applied Physiology. 9650 Wisconsin Ave., Washington 14, D.C.

Journal of Bone and Joint Surgery. The Fenway, Boston 15, Massachusetts.

Journal of Health, Physical Education and Recreation. 1201 Sixteenth St., N.W., Washington 6, D.C.

Journal of Pediatrics. 3207 Washington Blvd., St. Louis 3, Missouri.

Journal of School Health. 515 E. Main St., Kent, Ohio.

Journal of the Association for Physical and Mental Rehabilitation. Box 478, Montrose, New York.

Mental Hygiene. 10 Columbus Circle, New York 19, N.Y.

Physical Educator. 3747 N. Linwood Ave., Indianapolis 18, Indiana.

Recreation. 8 W. Eighth St., New York 11, N.Y.

Research Quarterly. 1201 Sixteenth St., N.W., Washington 6, D.C.

Today's Health. 535 N. Dearborn St., Chicago 10, Illinois.

INDEX

AAHPER Committee on Adapted Physical Education, 263
Abramson, Arthur S., 83, 114
Achilles flare, 90
Achilles tendon, 41, 45, 106, 187–188
Activities, criteria for selection of, 250–251
Adams' position, 110, 113
Adamson, G. T., 173, 181
Adaptations:
  anterior-posterior, 94–104
  compound, 102–104
  from faulty weight bearing, 87–90
  foot-ankle, 105–106
  lateral, 104–115
  spinal, lateral, 110
Adapted physical education, 7–14
  bases for, 10
  definition of, 9
  enlisting medical cooperation for, 256–260
  instructor, role of, 13
  nature and scope of program, 261–263
  objectives, 9
  and regular physical education, 254
Adapted physical education program:
  administration of, 265–280
  administrative process, 267–280
  assignment to and removal from, 274
  determining need for, 254–256
  organization of, 253–263
  purpose, 13
Adapted physical education programming, guide, 268
Adaptive changes, prevention of, 69
Adaptive shortening, connective tissues, 70

Administration, 253
Administrative handbook, 266
Administrators, school, 7
Admissions and dismissal, committee for, 275
Agonist, 26
Albinism, 127
Ambulation, early, 163
American Public Health Association Committee for Child Health, and the National Society for Prevention of Blindness, 127
Amputation, 70, 120, 126
  congenital, 120, 126
  surgical, 126
  traumatic, 126
Anatomical movements, 34–35
Anatomical position, 33
Anatomical positions and movements, list of, 34–35
Ankle, the, 142–145
Antagonist, 26
Anterior-posterior adaptations, 94–104
  compound, 102–104
Antigravity mechanism, muscles of, 74
Antigravity muscles, 74–76
Antigravity positions, 73
Anulus fibrosus, 151
Arch:
  longitudinal, 40, 82, 84, 87
  medial longitudinal, 42
  metatarsal, 82
  transverse, 82
Arch-height test, functional, 88
Asthma, 118, 134
Atlas, Charles, 171
Atrophy, 168
Auditory handicaps, exogenous, 129–130